HENRY HARRIS

Fellow of Lincoln College and Professor of Pathology in the University of Oxford

Nucleus and Cytoplasm

SECOND EDITION

CLARENDON PRESS . OXFORD
1970

Oxford University Press, Ely House, London W.1

GLASGOW NEW YORK TORONTO MELBOURNE WELLINGTON
CAPE TOWN SALISBURY IBADAN NAIROBI DAR ES SALAAM LUSAKA ADDIS ABABA
BOMBAY CALCUTTA MADRAS KARACHI LAHORE DACCA
KUALA LUMPUR SINGAPORE HONG KONG TOKYO

FIRST EDITION 1968
SECOND EDITION 1970

MADE AND PRINTED IN GREAT BRITAIN
BY WILLIAM CLOWES AND SONS, LIMITED
LONDON AND BECCLES

284299

Two roads diverged in a wood, and I—
I took the one less traveled by,
And that has made all the difference.

Robert Frost
from *The Road Not Taken*

Preface to the Second Edition

In the field of nucleo-cytoplasmic relationships, in which dozens of journals publish hundreds of papers each month, perhaps no apology is needed for the production of a second edition of this book so soon after the first. None the less, reliable information still comes slowly; and although some evidence that appeared strong in 1967 appears less strong in 1970, and some arguments then tenuous now appear to be correct, nothing has happened that seems to me to necessitate a fundamental revision of the main conclusions that I reached three years ago. I have done what I can to incorporate important new developments and hope that the book will continue to be of use to those who find the analytical approach attractive.

Oxford   HENRY HARRIS
Hilary, 1970

Preface to the First Edition

THE object of this book, originally delivered as a series of
lectures at the Sir William Dunn School of Pathology, University of Oxford, is to provide an introduction to some of the
salient problems in the field of nucleo-cytoplasmic relationships. The approach is analytical rather than didactic, but
it is intended to stimulate enthusiasm, not stifle it. I spend
most of my time doing experiments with animal cells, but I
have also worked with *Acetabularia* and *Vicia* on the one hand,
and with *Escherichia coli* and *Bacillus cereus* on the other; and
if I tend to view the simple diagram and the attractive
generalization with a critical eye, it is because a very varied
experience has made it clear to me that, with rare exceptions,
information comes slowly and accompanied, more often than
not, by a great deal of misinformation. But in this book I also
describe many of my own experiments, and I give my own
interpretations of them, and I make theories on the strength
of them; so there is more than enough to attract the attention
of other critical eyes. I do not, of course, imagine that all the
conclusions which I have reached will be universally popular,
but I like to think that many of them will now be regarded
as a closer approximation to the truth than might have been
the case a few years ago. I hope that the student who reads these
pages will come away with the conviction that some of the
most important problems in modern biology are far from solved;
for then, if he is lucky, he may later find that he can have
many hours of simple pleasure in attempting to solve them.

Oxford   HENRY HARRIS
Michaelmas 1967

Acknowledgements

PLATE 3a is reproduced by courtesy of Professors J.-E. Edström and W. Beermann and the editors of the *Journal of Cell Biology*, and Plate 3b by courtesy of Dr U. Clever and the editors of *Chromosoma*. Plates 2a and 2b were kindly supplied by Dr G. I. Schoefl. I wish to thank the editors of *Bacteriological Reviews* for permission to reproduce Fig. 3; the editor of *Nature* for permission to reproduce Fig. 4; and the editors of *Biochemical Journal*, *Journal of Cell Science*, and *Proceedings of the Royal Society*, for permission to reproduce many figures originally published by my colleagues and myself in these journals.

I am particularly indebted to Professors Edward Abraham and Joel Mandelstam who read the whole of the first edition of this book before publication. Their comments have greatly enhanced whatever value the work might have.

Contents

List of Plates

1. The expression of genetic information

1. Introduction

THESE days, when a biologist talks about genetic information he has in mind ordered sequences of nucleotides in DNA. When he talks about transfer of information he is probably thinking about the mechanism by which the instructions encoded in a sequence of DNA nucleotides are transported to some other site in the cell; and when he talks about expression of genetic information he usually means the mechanisms by which the biological significance of a particular sequence of DNA nucleotides becomes apparent in some aspect of cell behaviour. It is my view that we still know very little about the mechanisms by which information is transferred from the genes to specific sites in the cytoplasm, and still less about the mechanisms that determine whether and when this information is ultimately expressed. We know, of course, that the sequence of nucleotides in DNA is transcribed into some form of homologous sequence of nucleotides in RNA, and that this RNA forms a template for the synthesis of a corresponding sequence of amino acids in a polypeptide. But if, like the hedgehog, we can take comfort in the knowledge of this one big thing,[1] we should not blind ourselves to the fact that almost no part of the process is understood in any detail, and that the bare outline on which we are agreed does not provide us with satisfactory explanations for many of the most fundamental properties of living cells. We do not, at least in the case of eukaryotic cells, know:

(1) How the transcription of DNA is regulated and how precise this regulation is.

(2) Whether the genes are transcribed in any particular order, and if so, what determines this order.

(3) Whether the amount of a particular protein synthesized in the cell is related to the number of RNA copies that have been produced from the corresponding gene.

(4) Whether there is wide variation in the amount of RNA produced by different genes, and if so, what determines this variation.

(5) Whether there is any predictable relationship between the time at which a particular gene is transcribed and the time at which the corresponding protein is synthesized.

(6) In what form the RNA carrying the genetic instructions is transported to the cytoplasm of the cell, and whether this transport is itself regulated.

(7) Whether there are great differences in the lifetimes of different RNA templates in the cytoplasm of the cell and, if there are, what determines these differences.

(8) Whether there is any close relationship between the lifetime of an RNA template and the facility with which the synthesis of the corresponding protein can be initiated or suppressed.

(9) How the synthesis of a specific protein on a particular RNA template is switched on and off.

(10) Whether the rate of protein synthesis varies from template to template, and if so, what determines this variation.

When I say that we do not know the answers to these questions, I do not wish to imply that no attempts have been made to answer them. I mean simply that I do not find the evidence on these points compelling enough to permit me to feel confident that decisive answers have been obtained. But, in looking at this evidence, I cannot avoid the impression that some answers are very much more probable than others; and, in a sense, this work is an acknowledgement of the obligation to justify one's point of view.

2. Lessons from an enucleate cell

In 1926 Joachim Hämmerling, initially in collaboration with his teacher, Max Hartmann, began a series of investigations on the behaviour of the giant unicellular alga, *Acetabularia*, a member of the class *Dasycladaceae*. This plant, which is between 3 and 5 cm long when mature, contains a single nucleus located in the tip of one of the rhizoids at the base of its stalk. The giant cell develops from a small zygote: it forms first a stalk with rhizoids at its base and later a cap that has a characteristic shape for each species (Plates 1*a* and 1*b*). The nucleus of the cell can be removed simply by cutting off the rhizoid in which it is located; and the nucleus from one cell can readily be transplanted to another. Taking advantage of these features, Hämmerling carried out some simple experiments that proved to be decisive for our understanding of certain aspects of nucleo-cytoplasmic relationships. Hämmerling's original experiments were analysed in essentially descriptive terms;[2,3] but they have, over the last decade or so, been extensively elaborated by his pupils and others, using the more sophisticated methodology of contemporary biochemistry.[4] In some respects, the experiments that have been done on *Acetabularia* constitute the most precise analysis of nucleo-cytoplasmic interactions that has so far been made. I have no desire to belittle the enormous value of the work that has been done in recent years on *Escherichia coli* and other micro-organisms, especially in expanding the range and the power of genetical methods; but, on certain crucial questions, the evidence from micro-organisms is inconclusive, whereas the evidence from *Acetabularia* is not. A brief summary of the main observations that have been made on *Acetabularia* will, I think, at once establish their outstanding importance:

(1) The cap formed by a particular species of *Acetabularia* has a morphology that is characteristic of that species. The morphological features of the cap are determined by genes present in the cell nucleus: when the nucleus of one species of *Acetabularia* is transplanted into the cytoplasm of another, the transplanted nucleus eventually determines the formation of a cap that has the morphology characteristic of the species from which the nucleus was derived.[5-7]

(2) Formation of the cap is a complex morphogenetic event involving net synthesis of protein,[8] the synthesis of specific enzymes,[9-12] and the synthesis of specific polysaccharides.[13] The polysaccharide composition of the wall of the cap differs

from that found in the cell wall elsewhere;[13, 14] and when the cap is formed not only are the characteristic cap polysaccharides synthesized, but also the enzymes necessary for their synthesis.[11, 12] Cap formation involves changes in the rates of synthesis of certain other enzymes as well.[9, 10] although the roles that these other enzymes play in the morphogenetic process is not clear. The formation of the cap is thus a typical example of cellular differentiation, involving a precise regulation of the synthesis of specific proteins.

(3) A perfectly normal species-specific cap can be formed *de novo* many weeks after the nucleus has been removed from

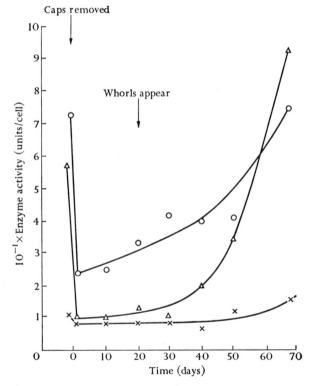

FIG. 1. Activities of three phosphatases, showing optima at pH 5 (◯), pH 8·5 (×), and pH 12 (△), in regenerating nucleate cells. Caps were removed from the cells and enzyme activities were measured during regeneration. Whorls are formed a little before the onset of cap formation, which is complete in 6–8 weeks. (From Spencer and Harris.[9])

the cell.[2, 4] The regulated synthesis of specific enzymes that accompanies cap formation in the presence of the nucleus also takes place in its absence[9-12] (Figs. 1 and 2). Moreover, it has been demonstrated in the case of two of the enzymes involved in the synthesis of the cap polysaccharides, that these enzymes are specified by the DNA in the cell nucleus.[15]

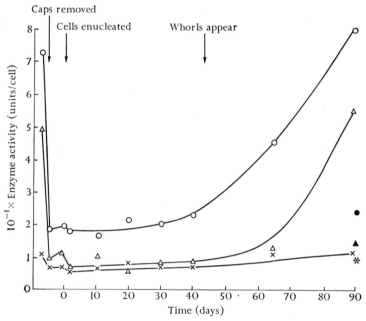

FIG. 2. Activities of three phosphatases, showing optima at pH 5 (○), pH 8·5 (×), and pH 12 (△), in regenerating *enucleate* cells. Caps were removed and the cells enucleated 8 days later. The activity of these three enzymes is also shown in cells that failed to regenerate: pH 5 (●), pH 8·5 (▲), pH 12 (∗). (From Spencer and Harris.[9])

(4) All the information necessary for the production of the cap passes from the nucleus to the cytoplasm long before the cap is normally formed. In *Acetabularia cliftonii* removal of the nucleus in a very young plant often provokes a very premature formation of the cap.[16] Premature caps may be produced by enucleation in this species at least 70 days before they are normally formed in the intact plant.[17] Premature caps may also be produced in other *Acetabularia* species by exposing the

cells to appropriate concentrations of certain plant hormones.[18] Both the formation of the cap and the synthesis of enzymes normally associated with cap formation can be induced prematurely by these hormones in enucleate cells.[18, 19] It is clear that the information for the production of the cap is delivered to the cytoplasm many days before it is used.

(5) Information for the production of the cap may be present in the cytoplasm of the cell without being expressed. Formation of the cap in *Acetabularia crenulata* may be suppressed if the cells are grown under conditions of restricted illumination. The cells continue growing under these conditions, and produce grossly elongated stalks without caps. If the nuclei are removed from these elongated stalks and the illumination is then increased, normal caps are formed on these enucleate stalks. The information for production of the cap is therefore present in the cytoplasm, but the expression of this information does not take place under conditions of inadequate illumination.[4]

(6) The information for the production of the cap is extremely stable. Enucleate stalks may be maintained for many weeks under conditions in which cap formation is inhibited, but even after this period of time the enucleate stalks will form caps when they are transferred to appropriate cultural conditions.[4]

While none of these observations deals directly with the metabolism of RNA in the cell, they none the less provide some very precise information about the behaviour in *Acetabularia* of that family of RNA molecules that is involved in the transfer of genetic information to the cytoplasm. The outstanding metabolic characteristic of the RNA molecules that carry the information for production of the cap is their persistence in the cytoplasm for long periods after removal of the nucleus. Although the original source of supply of these molecules has been eliminated by the removal of the nucleus, enough RNA to provide all the information necessary to produce a normal cap persists for many weeks, even under limiting cultural conditions. The cytoplasm of *Acetabularia*, like that of other organisms, contains active ribonucleases,[20] so that one obvious conclusion that can be drawn from these experiments is that the RNA that carries this genetic information is either present in the cytoplasm in a form that is very resistant to intracellular ribonucleases, or that this RNA is removed from the action of these enzymes in some way, perhaps by sequestration of the RNA or of the enzymes within specific cytoplasmic structures.

Two formal objections can be raised to this conclusion. The first is that the cytoplasm of *Acetabularia* contains DNA,[21] and that the RNA carrying the information for cap formation may be continually produced, or produced when required, from cytoplasmic DNA.[22] As far as the two reasonably well established forms of cytoplasmic DNA are concerned (the DNA of chloroplasts and mitochondria), this possibility can be dismissed. We know, from nuclear transplantation experiments, that the specific morphological features of the cap are determined by the cell nucleus, not by the chloroplasts or the mitochondria; and we know that at least two of the enzymes that are involved in the synthesis of cell wall polysaccharides, and that increase in amount when the cap is being formed, are also specified by the nucleus and not by the cytoplasm.[15] If the templates for these enzymes are produced from cytoplasmic DNA, we must envisage a cytoplasmic DNA that is a copy of the nuclear DNA. This idea implies that the transfer of information from nucleus to cytoplasm is, in some cases, effected by DNA not RNA, and that the specifications for at least some proteins are represented in both nuclear and cytoplasmic DNA. This model is unattractive for a variety of reasons. For example, there is no obvious reason why just those enzymes involved in the production of polysaccharides for the wall of the cap should have dual representation in both nuclear and cytoplasmic DNA; and if the phenomenon is more general, one is forced to consider the possibility of a widespread duplication of the genes in both nucleus and cytoplasm, a state of affairs that makes nonsense of most forms of genetic analysis, and for which there is no chemical evidence. Moreover, where there is good evidence that the specifications for a particular characteristic are encoded in cytoplasmic DNA, as, for example, in the case of the chloroplast, genetic analysis reveals a non-mendelian or cytoplasmic form of inheritance;[23] whereas nuclear transplantation experiments in *Acetabularia* indicate a simple and direct determination of the cap characteristics by the nucleus. It may be possible to construct some *ad hoc* scheme to overcome these difficulties, but there are at present no serious grounds for entertaining the idea that the information for production of the cap in *Acetabularia* is coded by cytoplasmic DNA.

The other possibility that could account for the persistence of this information in the enucleate cell is that the relevant RNA might be replicated in the cytoplasm. If the RNA templates could be copied in the cytoplasm, the information could persist without necessarily having a long life. The idea that normal cellular RNA templates might be replicated in the cytoplasm of the cell has a long history, but it does not at present command much support. There is, however, no doubt that a net synthesis of RNA can take place in the cytoplasm of *Acetabularia* after removal of the nucleus.[24, 25] Indeed, the great bulk of the RNA in *Acetabularia* is synthesized in the cell cytoplasm.[26] This cytoplasmic synthesis involves not only the RNA associated with chloroplasts and mitochondria, but also RNA outside these organelles.[26, 27] However, it is generally assumed, although it has not been proved, that all this RNA synthesis is primed by cytoplasmic DNA. This view is supported by the failure so far to detect in the cytoplasm of higher cells enzymes capable of replicating normal cellular RNA in the appropriate way. In any case, whether the persistence of the information is due to the cytoplasmic replication of RNA templates, or simply to their long life, it is clear that this information does not have to be continually replenished by the synthetic activity of the cell nucleus.

The second important conclusion that can be drawn from the *Acetabularia* experiments is that the actual expression of the information, that is, the synthesis of the specific protein, the synthesis of the specific polysaccharide, the morphogenetic event itself, is determined by events that take place in the cytoplasm, not in the nucleus. There is clearly no inevitable relationship between the time at which the genetic information is transferred from the nucleus to the cytoplasm and the time at which it is expressed. The RNA templates for the cap-forming enzymes may be delivered to the cytoplasm weeks before the enzymes are synthesized in appreciable amounts, and, in the enucleate cell, the formation of the cap with all its concomitant regulation of enzyme synthesis may be induced prematurely or greatly delayed by simple manipulations of the environment. The conclusion seems inescapable that the expression of the genetic information is effected by means of cytoplasmic regulatory mechanisms that initiate, regulate, and suppress the synthesis of proteins on pre-existing templates.

The experiments on *Acetabularia* also throw some light on two related questions: whether there is great variation in the lifetimes of different RNA templates, and whether this variation, if it exists, is closely related to the regulation of protein synthesis. Although the behaviour of only a few specific enzymes has been studied in enucleate *Acetabularia* cells, it must be borne in mind that the enucleate cell is capable of growth and regeneration as well as morphogenesis. A section of stalk containing the growing tip but no nucleus will, under appropriate conditions, regenerate both a new stalk and a cap.[2] These regenerative processes finally produce an essentially normal *Acetabularia* cell, although, of course, without a nucleus. Enucleate growth under these conditions cannot be an unregulated process, since the end result is a cell which, from both the morphological and physiological point of view, is essentially normal: all the normal cytoplasmic structures are present and all the normal cytoplasmic functions are carried out. We cannot, of course, exclude the possibility that some RNA templates, whose products we are not examining, are short lived; but it is clear that all the information required for the development of an essentially normal *Acetabularia* cell persists for many weeks after enucleation. Nor is it likely that the cessation of certain syntheses at particular stages of development, for example, the cessation of stalk growth when the cap is formed, is determined by the exhaustion of the templates that support these syntheses: under appropriate cultural conditions the stalk may be induced to continue growing long after it would normally have stopped. It therefore seems very improbable that the genetic information in the cytoplasm of *Acetabularia* has a wide spectrum of stability. Under clement cultural conditions the lifetime of most of this information must be measured in weeks at least. It is, of course, to be expected that on this time scale some variation in the life span of different RNA templates might occur, but it is hard to imagine that this variation could play any important role in regulating the synthesis of the great majority of the cytoplasmic proteins formed during the course of development. Information for the synthesis of specific proteins can certainly be present in the cytoplasm of the cell without being expressed; and this implies the existence of cytoplasmic regulatory mechanisms that suppress the synthesis of proteins without destroying their templates. In short, the study of *Acetabularia* tells us that growth and morphogenesis, which involve the controlled synthesis of many enzymes and many other proteins, are regulated not by mechanisms that govern the detailed transcription of the genes, but by mechanisms that operate in the cytoplasm of the cell.

3. Other enucleate cells

We have now to consider how far *Acetabularia* can be regarded as representative of higher animal and plant cells as a whole. It is at once obvious that *Acetabularia* is exceptional in some respects. It is, to begin with, of immense size for a single mononucleate cell and, as far as I am aware, no other cell that has so far been studied survives enucleation for so long, or with so little impairment of physiological function. But a closer examination of the peculiarities of *Acetabularia* suggests, I think, that these differences do not represent fundamental differences in cellular organization. *Acetabularia* remains mononucleate throughout most of its life cycle, despite its huge size, because nuclear division in this cell is delayed until a very late stage in its development. The nucleus increases in size throughout the many weeks of cell growth and reaches enormous proportions; but it remains a single nucleus until a mature cap has been formed. Only then does the giant nucleus produce the secondary nucleus from which, by repeated mitosis, the nuclei of the 7000–15 000 gametes are eventually produced.[4] It is thus merely the phenomenon of nuclear growth without nuclear division that distinguishes *Acetabularia* from many coenocytic organisms, which may also be single giant cells, but which contain many nuclei that divide as the cell grows. In other respects *Acetabularia* is a typical photosynthetic marine alga, and it would, *a priori*, be very surprising if its physiological processes proved to be regulated by mechanisms that differed in principle from those operating in other marine algae.

How far do enucleation studies in other cells support or contradict the conclusions drawn from *Acetabularia*? The number of cases that can be discussed is limited, for in most other cells enucleation presents more formidable technical problems than it does in *Acetabularia*; and it must be admitted at the outset that no other enucleate cell that has so far been examined can accomplish the complete regeneration and morphogenesis of which *Acetabularia* is capable. However, an examination of the behaviour of those cells in which the effects of enucleation have been studied indicates clearly that the differences between them and *Acetabularia* are matters of degree and do not reflect fundamentally different modes of biological organization. The cells of *Spyrogyra* survive enucleation for more than 2 months. They grow in the absence of the nucleus, form new cytoplasm containing specific cytoplasmic organelles, synthesize proteins, and carry out all their normal physiological functions.[28] No formal investigation has been made of the ability of the enucleate cytoplasm in *Spyrogyra* to regulate the synthesis of specific enzymes, but it is difficult to imagine that the enucleate cell does not possess this ability since, like *Acetabularia*, it is capable of ordered growth and ordered physiological function. The enucleated egg of the sea urchin *Arbacia* is capable of repeated cell division after parthenogenetic stimulation and, under suitable conditions, will form a blastula that may develop functional cilia.[29] In this case it has been shown that appropriate stimulation of the enucleate egg initiates a wave of protein synthesis in the quiescent cytoplasm comparable to that produced by fertilization in the normal egg.[30] This again shows that the information for the synthesis of these proteins is present in the egg some time before it is expressed, and that the cytoplasm itself contains the regulatory mechanisms necessary to determine the onset of this synthesis. Protein synthesis may be induced in frog oocytes by the administration of pituitary hormones. This induced protein synthesis is not abolished by enucleation of the oocyte. Indeed, for many hours, the rates of synthesis in nucleate and enucleate cells are indistinguishable.[31] Enucleated frog eggs,[32] the anucleate polar lobes of eggs of the mud snail *Ilyanassa obsoleta*,[33] and anucleate halves of eggs of the sea snail *Triton*[34] are all capable of unimpaired protein synthesis for long periods. Enucleate cells of *Stentor* can differentiate to produce partially formed mouth parts; they can form vacuoles, and they engage in virtually normal physiological activity for 3–4 days.[35] *Stentor* cells enucleated just before cell division can complete the division and form new daughter cells. In this case also there have been no biochemical studies, but the behaviour of the enucleate cells leaves little doubt that once again cytoplasmic regulation of protein synthesis must be taking place. The protozoon *Peranema trichophorum* can regenerate flagella in the absence of the nucleus.[36] Enucleate fragments of human tissue culture cells survive *in vitro* for up to 4 days.[37] These fragments move about, exhibit pinocytosis, and incorporate amino acids into protein.[38] Enucleate fragments of prospective pigment cells (melanoblasts) from the developing neural crest of urodele embryos also survive for long periods *in vitro*, and may undergo morphological differentiation to assume the dendritic character that is typical of the mature pigmented cell.[39] These fragments also synthesize pigment granules. Amoebas do not feed after enucleation and the synthetic abilities of the enucleate cytoplasm progressively diminish. None the less, synthesis of protein as measured by the incorporation of radioactive amino acids continues in the enucleate cytoplasm for many hours.[40] And finally, the mammalian reticulocyte continues to synthesize haemoglobin for some days after elimination of the cell nucleus, and the synthesis of the globin moiety is regulated by the availability of haem.[41]

The studies on enucleate cells other than *Acetabularia* are obviously fragmentary, but they none the less provide consistent evidence in support of the view that the templates for the synthesis of specific proteins persist in the cytoplasm of the cell for long periods after removal of the nucleus, and that the synthesis of the proteins on these templates is regulated by control mechanisms that operate in the cytoplasm itself.

4. Actinomycin D

A major extension of the range of this sort of investigation became possible with the introduction of the antibiotic actinomycin D. This compound, when used at a high enough concentration, combines with the DNA of the cell and inhibits its transcription into RNA. Actinomycin D has therefore been used to produce a form of 'physiological enucleation', a term that grossly over-simplifies the effects of the antibiotic. It cannot be over-emphasized that actinomycin D is an extremely toxic compound, and that, at concentrations that completely inhibit the transcription of DNA, it causes the rapid dissolution of most cells. When one finds, after administering a high dose of actinomycin D, that a particular physiological function or synthetic process is impaired, one cannot therefore conclude that this function or synthetic process is immediately or closely dependent upon the transcription of DNA. It has been shown that actinomycin D may produce drastic secondary effects; and where a cell is in the process of being killed by the antibiotic many processes may run down for reasons that are only remotely connected with the transcription of DNA. For the same reasons one cannot make any deductions about the rate of decay of the templates for protein synthesis from the changes produced by actinomycin D in the rate of this synthesis. The synthesis of proteins may become progressively impaired by the antibiotic for reasons that have nothing to do with the decay of the templates. This is not merely a speculative possibility: it has been shown in one type of cell that the fall in the rate of protein synthesis induced by the administration of actinomycin D can be reversed simply by adding glucose to the medium.[42] Moreover, it is now clear that high concentrations of actinomycin D may induce extensive degradation of all families of RNA in the cell,[43] so that deductions about the normal life span of RNA templates made from observations on actinomycin D-poisoned cells are hazardous in the extreme.

On the other hand, if a particular physiological function persists for long periods in the presence of high concentrations of actinomycin D, this is presumptive evidence that the function in question is not immediately dependent on the transcription of DNA. If the synthesis of a particular protein continues after virtually all RNA synthesis has been suppressed by actinomycin D, one can probably conclude that the templates for the synthesis of this protein are stable in the sense that they do not have to be continually replaced by fresh synthesis; and if the synthesis of a particular protein can be regulated under such conditions, one can probably conclude that the regulatory mechanisms are cytoplasmic in the sense that they do not operate via transcription of the DNA. Thus, with actinomycin D, only the positive result, the persistence of function in the absence of RNA synthesis, has probative value; the negative result, the impairment of function, is, without other evidence, uninterpretable.

So much work has been done with actinomycin D since its introduction some years ago, that it would be difficult to give a complete catalogue of cases in which synthesis of a protein has been initiated in the presence of high concentrations of actinomycin D, or in which synthesis of a protein persists and continues to be regulated in the presence of the antibiotic. The following list is a collection of the more convincing examples that have come to my notice: synthesis of protein induced by fertilization in sea urchin eggs,[44, 45] and division of the eggs to the 16-cell stage with differentiation of animal and vegetal territories;[46] synthesis of protein in the starfish egg from fertilization to the formation of the blastula, and formation of the gastrula if the antibiotic is administered after ciliation of the blastula;[47] synthesis of the enzymes trehalose-6-phosphate synthetase, uridine diphosphate glucose pyrophosphorylase and uridine diphosphate galactose polysaccharide transferase during the development of the slime mould *Dictyostelium*;[48–50] synthesis of serine dehydrase in mammalian liver;[51, 52] induction of apoferritin in mammalian liver by the administration of iron;[53] differentiation of amphibian myoblasts into muscle cells containing striated myofibrils;[54] synthesis of protein in rat heart cells in culture;[55] synthesis of a specific plasma phosphoprotein induced in male chickens by the administration of diethylstilboestrol;[56] synthesis of glutamine synthetase in developing embryonic chick neural retina;[57] synthesis of specific lens proteins in the mammalian eye;[58, 59] stimulation of protein synthesis in isolated rat diaphragm by growth hormone;[60] depression of the rate of protein synthesis in the liver of adrenalectomized rats by corticosteroids;[61] stimulation of protein synthesis in the isolated rat diaphragm and in rat heart muscle by insulin;[62, 63] the growth response produced in the chick comb by androgens;[64] synthesis of thyroglobulin in the thyroid gland;[64] differentiation[66] and production of amylase[65] in developing pancreatic cells of the mouse embryo;

PLATE I

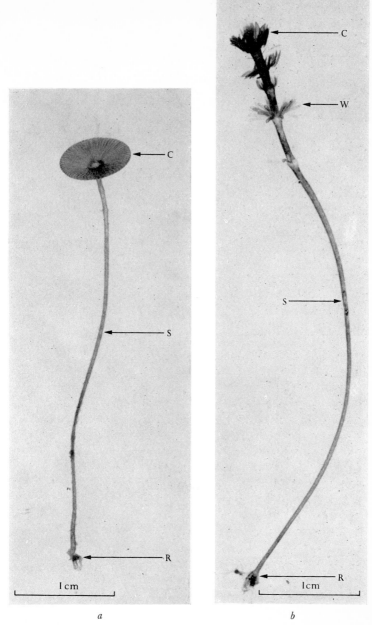

a   *b*

a. Acetabularia mediterranea cell. C, cap; S, stalk; R, rhizoid containing
the nucleus.

b. Acetabularia crenulata cell. C, cap; W, whorls, which are formed
shortly before the development of the cap; S, stalk; R, rhizoid
containing the nucleus.

PLATE 2

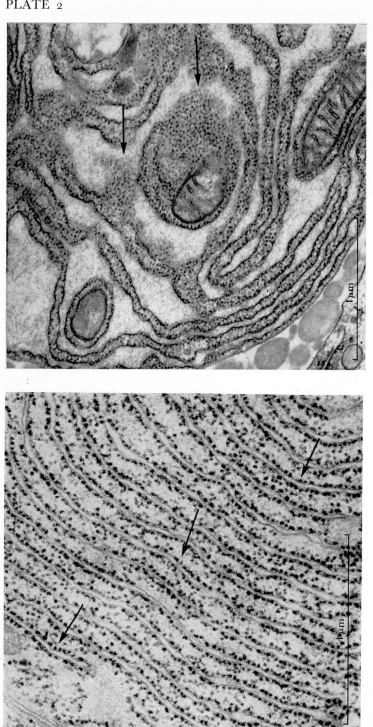

a. Cross-section of the endoplasmic reticulum (internal membrane system) of a cell from the lactating mammary gland of the rat. The ribosomes, shown as dark dots, are attached to the membranes of the reticulum as a single layer. This is clearly seen at the sites shown by the arrows. (By courtesy of Dr G. I. Schoefl.)

b. Section from a 'plasma-cell' in the lymphatic tissue of the gut of a mouse. Such cells are thought to be engaged in the secretion of antibodies. The arrows show parts of the endoplasmic reticulum sectioned *en face*. It can be seen that the membranes are studded with a close-set array of single ribosomes. (By courtesy of Dr G. I. Schoefl.)

PLATE 3

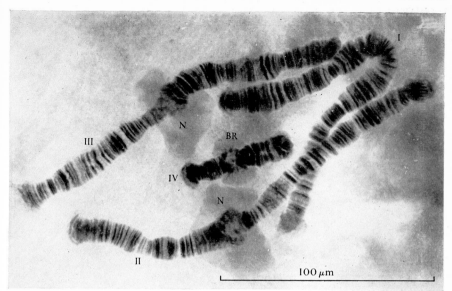

a

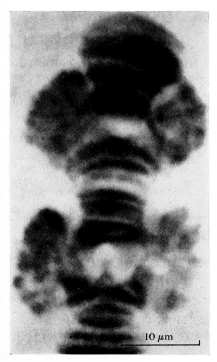

a. The polytene salivary gland chromosomes (I, II, III, IV) of *Chironomus tentans*. The nucleoli (N) and a large puff (Balbiani ring) (BR) are shown. (By courtesy of Prof. J.-E. Edström and Prof. W. Beermann.)

b. Two large puffs (Balbiani rings) on chromosome IV of the salivary gland of *Chironomus tentans*. (By courtesy of Dr U. Clever.)

b

PLATE 4

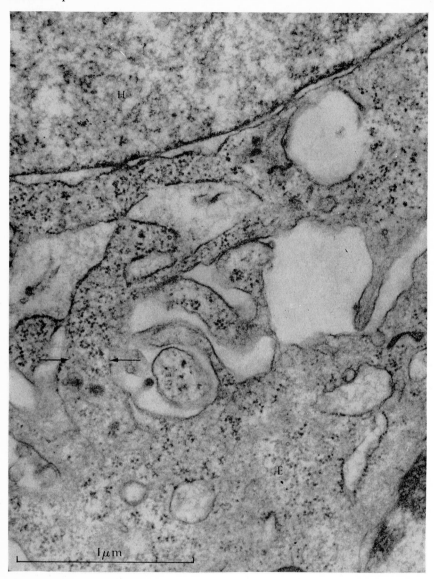

A delicate cytoplasmic bridge, shown by the arrows, between a HeLa cell (H) and an Ehrlich ascites cell (E). (From Schneeberger and Harris[8] (chap. 5).)

synthesis of a specific enzyme, 'cocoonase', in specialized glands of the silk moth;[68] initiation of haemoglobin synthesis in chick embryo explants;[69] and the anamnestic formation of antibodies.[70, 71]

Since it is very difficult to inhibit the transcription of DNA completely with actinomycin D, results obtained by the use of this compound are less free from objection than those obtained by enucleation: it can always be argued that the template for the particular protein being studied continues to be produced in the small amount of RNA that is synthesized in the presence of actinomycin D. This argument can hardly apply to those cases where protein synthesis as a whole has been measured, but it could apply to those in which the synthesis of a single specific protein has been examined. Moreover, the possibility must always be considered that accumulation of a protein may result, not only from an increase in the rate of its synthesis, but also from a decrease in the rate of its degradation.[72, 73] The number of cases listed above (and there are many others), the wide range of the biological material, and the very different kinds of proteins studied, make it difficult to believe that they are all specified by that small group of genes whose transcription is relatively resistant to the action of actinomycin D; and in some of these cases there is no possibility that the observations could be accounted for by a reduction in the rate of protein degradation.

It therefore seems reasonable to conclude that in the higher cells of plants and animals, in both protozoa and metazoa, the principles that have been shown to operate in *Acetabularia* are, in general, applicable. The time at which a particular gene is transcribed into RNA has no immediate connection with the time at which this RNA is translated into protein. The templates for protein synthesis pass to the cytoplasm in a form that is, on the whole, resistant to intracellular degradation; these templates persist in the cytoplasm for long periods after removal of the nucleus. Initiation, regulation, and suppression of protein synthesis on these essentially stable templates is effected by cytoplasmic mechanisms that can operate perfectly well in the absence of the nucleus.

We must now examine to what extent these general principles are also applicable to micro-organisms.

REFERENCES

1. BERLIN, I. (1953). *The hedgehog and the fox.* Weidenfeld & Nicolson, London.
2. HÄMMERLING, J. (1934). Regenerationsversuche an kernhaltigen und kernlosen Zellteilen von *Acetabularia Wettsteinii. Biol. Zbl.* **54,** 650.
3. HÄMMERLING, J. (1934). Über formbildende Substanzen bei *Acetabularia mediterranea,* ihre räumliche und zeitliche Verteilung und ihre Herkunft. *Wilhelm Roux Arch. EntwMech. Org.* **131,** 1.
4. HÄMMERLING, J. (1963). Nucleo-cytoplasmic interactions in *Acetabularia* and other cells. *A. Rev. Pl. Physiol.* **14,** 65.
5. HÄMMERLING, J. (1953). Nucleo-cytoplasmic relationship in the development of *Acetabularia. Int Rev. Cytol.* **2,** 475.
6. WERZ, G. (1961). Zur Frage der Herkunft und Verteilung cytoplasmatischer Ribonucleinsäure und ihrer Beziehungen zu "morphogenetischen Substanzen" bei *Acetabularia mediterranea. Z. Naturf.* **16b,** 126.
7. ZETSCHE, K. (1962). Die Aktivität implantierter Zellkerne von *Acetabularia* bei aufgehobener Photosynthese. *Naturwissenschaften* **17,** 404.
8. HÄMMERLING, J., CLAUSS, H., KECK, K., RICHTER, G., and WERZ, G. (1958). Growth and protein synthesis in nucleated and enucleated cells. *Expl Cell Res.* Suppl. **6,** 210.
9. SPENCER, T. and HARRIS, H. (1964). Regulation of enzyme synthesis in an enucleate cell. *Biochem. J.* **91,** 282.
10. TRIPLETT, E. L., STEENS-LIEVENS, A., and BALTUS, E. (1965). Rates of synthesis of acid phosphatases in nucleate and enucleate *Acetabularia* fragments. *Expl Cell Res.* **38,** 366.
11. ZETSCHE, K. (1965). Übertragung und Realisierung genetischer Information bei der Morphogenese von *Acetabularia. Ber. dt. bot. Ges.* **78,** 87.
12. ZETSCHE, K. (1966). Regulation der UDP-Glucose 4-Epimerase Synthese in kernhaltigen und kernlosen Acetabularien. *Biochim. biophys. Acta* **124,** 332.
13. WERZ, G. (1963). Vergleichende Zellmembrananalysen bei verschiedenen Dasycladaceen. *Planta* **60,** 322.
14. ZETSCHE, K. (1967). Unterschiedliche Zusammensetzung von Stiel- und Hutzellwand bei *Acetabularia mediterranea. Planta* **76,** 326.
15. ZETSCHE, K. (1968). Regulation der UDPG-Pyrophosphorylase-Aktivität in *Acetabularia.* I. Morphogenese und UDPG-Pyrophosphorylase-Synthese in kernhaltigen und kernlosen Zellen. *Z. Naturf.* **23b,** 369.
16. WERZ, G. (1965). Determination and realization of morphogenesis in *Acetabularia. Brookhaven Symp. Biol.* No. 18, 185.
17. HÄMMERLING, J. and ZETSCHE, K. (1966). Zeitliche Steuerung der Formbildung von *Acetabularia. Umschau* **15,** 489.
18. ZETSCHE, K. (1963). Der Einfluss von Kinetin und Gibberellin auf die Morphogenese kernhaltiger und kernloser Acetabularien. *Planta* **59,** 624.

19. SPENCER, T. (1968). Effect of kinetin on the phosphatase enzymes of *Acetabularia*. *Nature, Lond.* **217,** 62.
20. SCHWEIGER, H.-G. (1966). Ribonuclease-Aktivität in *Acetabularia*. *Planta* **68,** 247.
21. GIBOR, A. and IZAWA, M. (1963). The DNA content of the chloroplasts of *Acetabularia*. *Proc. natn. Acad. Sci. U.S.A.* **50,** 1164.
22. SCHWEIGER, H.-G. and BERGER, S. (1964). DNA-dependent RNA synthesis in chloroplasts of *Acetabularia*. *Biochim. biophys. Acta* **87,** 533.
23. SAGER, R. (1965). On the evolution of genetic systems. *Evolving genes and proteins* (Eds. V. BRYSON and H. J. VOGEL), p. 591. Academic Press, New York.
24. SCHWEIGER, H.-G. and BREMER, H. J. (1960). Nachweis cytoplasmatischer Ribonukleinsäuresynthese in kernlosen Acetabularien. *Expl Cell Res.* **20,** 617.
25. SCHWEIGER, H.-G. and BREMER, H. J. (1961). Cytoplasmatische RNS-synthese in kernlosen Acetabularien. *Biochim. biophys. Acta* **51,** 50.
26. SCHWEIGER, H.-G., DILLARD, W. L., GIBOR, A., and BERGER, S. (1967). RNA-Synthesis in *Acetabularia*. *Protoplasma* **64,** 1.
27. JANOWSKI, M., BONOTTO, S., and BOLOUKHÈRE, M. (1969). Ribosomes of *Acetabularia mediterranea*. *Biochim. biophys. Acta* **174,** 525.
28. HÄMMERLING, J. (1959). Spirogyra und Acetabularia (Ein Vergleich ihrer Fähigkeiten nach Entfernung des Kernes). *Biol. Zbl.* **78,** 703.
29. HARVEY, E. B. (1940). A comparison of the development of nucleate and non-nucleate eggs of *Arbacia punctulata*. *Biol. Bull. mar. biol. Lab.*, *Woods Hole* **79,** 166.
30. BRACHET, J., FICQ, A., and TENCER, R. (1963). Amino acid incorporation into proteins of nucleate and anucleate fragments of sea urchin eggs: effect of parthenogenetic activation. *Expl Cell Res.* **32,** 168.
31. ECKER, R. E., SMITH, L. D., and SUBTELNY, S. (1968). Kinetics of protein synthesis in enucleate frog oocytes. *Science N.Y.* **160,** 1115.
32. SMITH, L. D. and ECKER, R. E. (1965). Protein synthesis in enucleated eggs of *Rana pipiens*. *Science, N.Y.* **150,** 777.
33. CLEMENT, A. C. and TYLER, A. (1967). Protein-synthesizing activity of the anucleate polar lobe of the mud snail *Ilyanassa obsoleta*. *Science, N.Y.* **158,** 1457.
34. TIEDEMANN, H. and TIEDEMANN, H. (1954). Einbau von $^{14}CO_2$ in gefurchte und ungefurchte Eihälften und in verschiedene Entwicklungsstadien von *Triton*. *Naturwissenschaften* **41,** 535.
35. TARTAR, V. (1961). *The biology of* Stentor, p. 297. Pergamon Press, Oxford.
36. TAMM, S. L. (1969). The effect of enucleation on flagellar regeneration in the protozoon *Peranema trichophorum*. *J. Cell Sci.* **4,** 171.
37. GOLDSTEIN, L., CAILLEAU, R., and CROCKER, T. T. (1960). Nuclear-cytoplasmic relationships in human cells in tissue culture. *Expl Cell Res.* **19,** 332.
38. GOLDSTEIN, L., MICOU, J., and CROCKER, T. T. (1960). Nuclear-cytoplasmic relationships in human cells in tissue culture. *Biochim. biophys. Acta* **45,** 82.

39. WILDE, C. E. (1961). The differentiation of vertebrate pigment cells. *Adv. Morphogenesis* **1**, 287.

40. MAZIA, D. and PRESCOTT, D. M. (1955). The role of the nucleus in protein synthesis in *Amoeba. Biochim. biophys. Acta* **17**, 23.

41. BRUNS, G. P. and LONDON, I. H. (1965). The effect of hemin on the synthesis of globin. *Biochem. biophys. Res. Commun.* **18**, 236.

42. HONIG, G. R. and RABINOWITZ, M. (1965). Actinomycin D: inhibition of protein synthesis unrelated to effect on template RNA synthesis. *Science, N.Y.* **149**, 1504.

43. WIESNER, R., ACS, G., REICH, E., and SHAFIQ, A. (1965). Degradation of ribonucleic acid in mouse fibroblasts treated with actinomycin. *J. Cell Biol.* **27**, 47.

44. GROSS, P. R. and COUSINEAU, G. H. (1963). Effects of actinomycin D on macromolecule synthesis and early development in sea urchin eggs. *Biochem. biophys. Res. Commun.* **10**, 321.

45. GROSS, P. R., MALKIN, L. I., and MOYER, W. A. (1964). Templates for the first proteins of embryonic development. *Proc. natn. Acad. Sci. U.S.A.* **51**, 407.

46. GIUDICE, G. and HÖRSTADIUS, S. (1965). Effect of actinomycin D on the segregation of animal and vegetal potentialities in the sea urchin egg. *Expl Cell Res.* **39**, 117.

47. BARROS, C., HAND, G. S., and MONROY, A. (1966). Control of gastrulation in the starfish *Asterias forbesii. Expl Cell Res.* **43**, 167.

48. SUSSMAN, M. and SUSSMAN, R. R. (1965). The regulatory program for UDP galactose polysaccharide transferase activity during slime mold cytodifferentiation: requirement for specific synthesis of ribonucleic acid. *Biochim. biophys. Acta* **108**, 463.

49. ROTH, R., ASHWORTH, J. M., and SUSSMAN, M. (1968). Periods of genetic transcription required for the synthesis of three enzymes during cellular slime mold development. *Proc. natn. Acad. Sci. U.S.A.* **59**, 1235.

50. NEWELL, P. C. and SUSSMAN, M. (1969). Uridine diphosphate glucose pyrophosphorylase in *Dictyostelium discoideum.* Stability and developmental fate. *J. biol. Chem.* **244**, 2990.

51. PITOT, H. C., PERAINO, C., LAMAR, C., and KENNAN, A. L. (1965). Template stability of some enzymes in rat liver and hepatoma. *Proc. natn. Acad. Sci. U.S.A.* **54**, 845.

52. JOST, J.-P., KHAIRALLAH, E. A., and PITOT, H. C. (1968). Studies on the induction and repression of enzymes in rat liver. V. Regulation of the rate of synthesis and degradation of serine dehydratase by dietary amino acids and glucose. *J. biol. Chem.* **243**, 3057.

53. DRYSDALE, J. W. and MUNRO, H. N. (1965). Failure of actinomycin D to prevent induction of liver apoferritin after iron administration. *Biochim. biophys. Acta* **103**, 185.

54. DUPRAT, A.-M., ZALTA, J.-P., and BEETSCHEN, J.-C. (1966). Action de l'actinomycine D sur la differenciation de divers types de cellules embryonnaires de l'amphibien *Pleurodeles waltlii* en culture *in vitro. Expl Cell Res.* **43**, 358.

55. McCARL, R. L. and SHALER, R. C. (1969). The effects of actinomycin D on protein synthesis and beating in cultured rat heart cells. *J. Cell Biol.* **40,** 850.

56. GREENGARD, O., GORDON, M., SMITH, M. A. and Acs, G. (1964). Studies on the mechanism of diethylstilbestrol-induced formation of phosphoprotein in male chickens. *J. biol. Chem.* **239,** 2079.

57. KIRK, D. L. (1965). The role of RNA synthesis in the production of glutamine synthetase by developing chick neural retina. *Proc. natn. Acad. Sci. U.S.A.* **54,** 1345.

58. PAPACONSTANTINOU, J., STEWART, J. A., and KOEHN, P. V. (1966). A localized stimulation of lens protein synthesis by actinomycin D. *Biochim. biophys. Acta* **114,** 428.

59. SPECTOR, A. and KINOSHITA, J. H. (1965). The effect of actinomycin D and puromycin upon RNA and protein metabolism in calf lens. *Biochim. biophys. Acta* **95,** 561.

60. MARTIN, T. E. and YOUNG, F. G. (1965). An *in vitro* action of human growth hormone in the presence of actinomycin D. *Nature, Lond.* **208,** 684.

61. BREUER, C. B. and DAVIS, F. F. (1964). Limited action of actinomycin D on protein synthesis in adrenalectomized rats. *Biochem. biophys. Res. Commun.* **14,** 215.

62. WOOL, I. G. and MOYER, A. N. (1964). Effect of actinomycin and insulin on the metabolism of isolated rat diaphragm. *Biochim. Biophys. Acta* **91,** 248.

63. WOOL, I. G. and CAVICCHI, P. (1966). Insulin regulation of protein synthesis by muscle ribosomes: effect of the hormone on translation of messenger RNA for a regulatory protein. *Proc. natn. Acad. Sci. U.S.A.* **56,** 991.

64. TALWAR, G. P., MODI, S., and RAO, K. N. (1965). DNA-dependent synthesis of RNA is not implicated in growth response of chick comb to androgens. *Science, N.Y.* **150,** 1315.

65. SEED, R. W. and GOLDBERG, I. H. (1965). Biosynthesis of thyroglobulin. *J. biol. Chem.* **240,** 764.

66. WESSELLS, N. K. and WILT, F. H. (1965). Action of actinomycin D on exocrine pancreas cell differentiation. *J. molec. Biol.* **13,** 767.

67. RUTTER, W. J., WESSELLS, N. K., and GROBSTEIN, C. (1964). Control of specific synthesis in the developing pancreas. *J. natn. Cancer Inst. Monograph* **13,** p. 51.

68. KAFATOS, F. C. and REICH, J. (1968). Stability of differentiation-specific and nonspecific messenger RNA in insect cells. *Proc. natn. Acad. Sci. U.S.A.* **60,** 1458.

69. WILT, F. H. (1965). Regulation of the initiation of chick embryo hemoglobin synthesis. *J. molec. Biol.* **12,** 331.

70. SMILEY, J. D., HEARD, J. G., and ZIFF, M. (1964). Effect of actinomycin on RNA synthesis and antibody formation in the anamnestic response *in vitro*. *J. exp. Med.* **119,** 881.

71. GELLER, B. D. and SPIERS, R. S. (1964). Failure of actinomycin D to inhibit antitoxin production to a challenging injection of antigen. *Proc. Soc. exp. Biol. Med.* **117,** 782.

72. SCHIMKE, R. T. (1964). The importance of both synthesis and degradation in the control of arginase levels in rat liver. *J. biol. Chem.* **239,** 3808.

73. SCHIMKE, R. T., SWEENEY, E. W., and BERLIN, C. M. (1964). An analysis of the kinetics of rat liver tryptophan pyrrolase induction: the significance of both enzyme synthesis and degradation. *Biochem. biophys. Res. Commun.* **15,** 214.

2. The genetic operator model

1. The theory of Jacob and Monod

In 1961 there appeared in the *Journal of Molecular Biology* a paper by François Jacob and Jacques Monod entitled 'Genetic regulatory mechanisms in the synthesis of proteins'.[1] In this paper a model for the regulation of protein synthesis is described that is diametrically opposed to the principal conclusions reached in Chapter 1. In its simplest form this model envisages that the mechanisms that regulate the synthesis of protein do not operate in the cytoplasm of the cell where the protein is synthesized (the 'cytoplasmic operator' model), but act directly on the genes by governing the transcription of the DNA into RNA (the 'genetic operator' model). The evidence on which Jacob and Monod based their theory was limited to experiments on bacteria and very largely to their own experiments on the regulation of the synthesis of the inducible enzyme β-galactosidase in *Escherichia coli*. A consideration of their famous paper cannot be avoided in any discussion on the mechanism of gene action, not only because it is, in itself, an exposé of great intellectual brilliance, but also because it advances a point of view that is clearly at variance with an apparently well-established body of evidence in higher cells. If the 'genetic operator' model proposed by Jacob and Monod is true for bacteria, and the 'cytoplasmic operator' model is true for higher cells, as the evidence reviewed in Chapter 1 appears to indicate, then one must conclude that the mechanisms responsible for governing the regulation of protein synthesis in higher cells are different *in principle* from those that regulate protein synthesis in bacteria; and this would be a biological generalization of the greatest importance.

Jacob and Monod allowed that the genetical experiments
that formed the main part of their paper were compatible
with either the 'genetic' or the 'cytoplasmic' operator model;
but they considered that, on the whole, the evidence in bacteria,
and especially the biochemical evidence, strongly favoured the
'genetic' model. Four lines of argument were advanced in
support of this view.

(1) The expression of clusters of related genes in certain
Gram negative bacteria sometimes occurs co-ordinately; that is
to say, the synthesis of all the enzymes in a particular metabolic
sequence, which may be represented on the bacterial chromosome by a group of adjacent, or closely apposed, genes, may be
initiated or suppressed at one step. This fact was thought to be
difficult to reconcile with the cytoplasmic operator model if
only because of the size that the relevant cytoplasmic template
would have to attain. Making certain assumptions, Jacob and
Monod calculated that co-ordinate regulation of a group of
three enzymes each having a molecular weight of 60 000 would
require a template of molecular weight 1.8×10^6; and since
co-ordinate regulation of groups of up to eight enzymes was
known to occur, it was argued that the size of some templates
would have to be substantially larger. This was thought to be
unlikely, since, at the time, the RNA of *E. coli* was not thought
to contain polyribonucleotides of a molecular weight ex-
ceeding 10^6.

(2) The induction of the enzyme β-galactosidase by an
appropriate inducer takes place in *E. coli* within 3 min;[2] and
the enzyme is then synthesized at a maximal rate.[3] When the
inducer is removed, synthesis of the enzyme promptly ceases
(Fig. 3). If regulation of this enzyme was effected by mechanisms operating at the genetic level, one might expect that the
kinetics of induction would be mimicked by the introduction
of the β-galactosidase gene into a cell which lacked it, and that
the kinetics of the cessation of synthesis would be mimicked
by removal of the gene from the cell. When the structural
gene for β-galactosidase was transferred by sexual conjugation
from a cell that possessed the gene into one that lacked it,
it was indeed found that synthesis of the enzyme in the recipient
cell began within a couple of minutes, and that the enzyme
was synthesized at the maximal rate.[4] Direct removal of the

gene from the cell is hardly possible in bacteria; but it was thought that indirect removal of the gene might be achieved if a large dose of radioactive phosphorus was introduced into the chromosome bearing the β-galactosidase gene before this chromosome was transferred to a recipient cell that lacked it. It was assumed that the decay of the radioactive

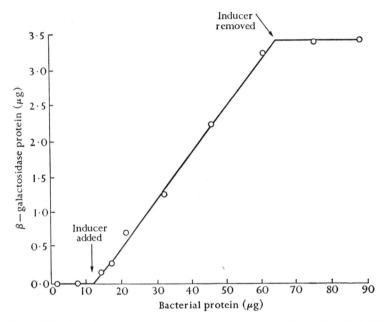

FIG. 3. Kinetics of induced synthesis of β-galactosidase in *Escherichia coli*. A differential plot expressing the accumulation of β-galactosidase as a function of the increase in the mass of cells in a growing culture. (Redrawn from Cohn.[3])

phosphorus would destroy the gene *in situ*. When this experiment was performed it was found that the ability of the recipient cell to synthesize β-galactosidase diminished as decay of the radioactive phosphorus caused progressive disintegration of the chromosome.[4] This result was interpreted to mean that integrity of the chromosome was essential for synthesis of β-galactosidase to occur.

(3) Infection of *E. coli* with certain virulent bacteriophages φ11, T2 and T4, results in rapid cessation of the synthesis of virtually all bacterial proteins, including β-galactosidase.[5-7]

These phages induce depolymerization of the bacterial DNA.[8] Infection of *E. coli* with phage λ, however, allows β-galactosidase synthesis to continue almost until the time of lysis: this phage does not depolymerize the bacterial DNA.[9] These findings were thought to lend further support to the idea that integrity of the bacterial chromosome was essential for protein synthesis.

(4) In *E. coli* the pyrimidine analogue 5-fluorouracil is rapidly incorporated into RNA. When the alkaline phosphatase made by the bacterium in the presence of 5-fluorouracil was examined, it was found to be abnormally sensitive to inactivation by heat.[10] In a strain of *E. coli* that synthesized β-galactosidase constitutively (that is, even in the absence of an appropriate inducer) the rate of synthesis of active enzyme was rapidly reduced by 5-fluorouracil, but a protein that cross-reacted with anti-β-galactosidase antiserum continued to be produced.[11] This protein was thought to be a structurally modified, inactive form of β-galactosidase. In its effects on protein synthesis 5-fluorouracil was said to be remarkable in two respects. It changed the properties of the proteins synthesized in its presence almost immediately (abnormal enzymes were thought to be synthesized virtually from the time of addition of the analogue); and the degree of abnormality of these proteins remained constant with time. These characteristics were thought to indicate that *all* the alkaline phosphatase or β-galactosidase molecules made after the addition of 5-fluorouracil were abnormal; and it was therefore deduced that these molecules could not have been made on templates present in the cell before the analogue was added. If true, this conclusion obviously implied that the act of transcription of a particular gene directly and immediately influenced the synthesis of the corresponding protein.

How convincing are these four lines of argument in the light of subsequent experiment?

2. *Examination of the evidence*

(1) As Jacob and Monod themselves admit, the argument based on the assumption that *E. coli* does not contain any RNA molecules big enough to form a template for the co-ordinate regulation of a metabolically related group of enzymes is a very weak one. Measurements of the molecular

weight of RNA are fraught with difficulties, and no confident statement can be made, even today, about the true dimensions of some families of RNA molecules, especially when they have a low order of secondary structure.[12, 13] I shall have occasion at a later stage to discuss in some detail the errors inherent in attempts to deduce the size of RNA molecules from their sedimentation behaviour; but at this stage it is enough to say that the idea of a 'polycistronic' template, that is, one that can specify the amino acid sequences of a group of related proteins, now enjoys considerable popularity.

(2) The observations on cells that have received the β-galactosidase gene by conjugation, and from which the gene has supposedly been removed by decay of radioactive phosphorus in the chromosome, constitute a more impressive argument in support of the genetic operator model. Of the two groups of experiments, those involving removal of the gene are obviously the more telling. The fact that β-galactosidase synthesis in the recipient cell begins within 2 or 3 min of receipt of the gene is compatible with almost any model for the regulatory process, provided that the gene is transcribed very soon after it enters the recipient cell. Two or three minutes may represent as much as one-tenth of the generation time of an *E. coli* cell, so that there is ample opportunity during the lag phase that precedes synthesis of the enzyme for virtually any form of regulation to occur. Moreover, as the authors of the conjugation experiment themselves point out,[4] the possibility is not excluded that RNA, as well as DNA, might be transferred from one cell to another during the conjugation process. Indeed, more recent experiments suggest that the quantity of RNA that could be transferred during conjugation might amount to between 30 per cent and 100 per cent of the quantity of DNA transferred.[14]

The observation that synthesis of β-galactosidase in the recipient cell begins, and continues for some time, at the maximal rate also provides no evidence about the site of regulation. Jacob and Monod reason that this finding indicates either that the gene produces templates that act as short-lived intermediates, or that the gene produces a limited number of templates and then stops functioning. But this reasoning applies only if there is a fixed relationship between the number of templates produced and the amount of enzyme formed; and this we do not know. In animal and plant cells it is clear that templates may be present in the cytoplasm of the cell without being expressed; and when synthesis of a particular protein takes place we do not know whether all the cytoplasmic templates for that protein are translated, or only some of them. And we certainly do not know that the maximum rate of synthesis of a particular protein in the whole cell is determined only and simply by the number of templates for that protein that it contains.

The experiments in which the bacterial chromosome bearing the β-galactosidase gene is destroyed by decay of radioactive phosphorus are, in principle, analogous to the enucleation experiments that have been carried out on higher cells. In the latter, as I described in Chapter 1, it is in general the case that synthesis of specific proteins continues after removal of the nucleus; and in many instances it has been shown that this synthesis can be regulated by the enucleate cytoplasm. At first glance the results of the radioactive phosphorus decay experiments appear to indicate that this is not the case for bacteria, at least for the enzyme β-galactosidase in *E. coli*. In the experiments described by Jacob and Monod[4] the zygote that has received the radioactive chromosome bearing the β-galactosidase gene rapidly loses its ability to synthesize the enzyme as decay of the radioactive phosphorus takes place. However, these experiments have been re-examined by McFall,[15] who showed that the results were open to a quite different interpretation. In order to study the effect of the radioactive decay, the cells are maintained for the required period in a frozen state, and then thawed to permit assay of the enzyme. Glycerol is normally added to the medium to prevent extensive disruption of the cell by the process of freezing and thawing; and this was done in the experiments described by Jacob and Monod.[4] However, glycerol is a metabolizable source of carbon for *E. coli*, and, like other sources of carbon, it suppresses the induced formation of β-galactosidase, a phenomenon originally called the 'glucose' effect and now usually described as an example of 'catabolite repression'. McFall showed that if glycol, which is not a metabolizable source of carbon, is used instead of glycerol, then the ability of the radioactive zygotes to synthesize β-galactosidase is relatively resistant to decay of the isotope in the bacterial chromosome. Even when this decay has reduced the viability of the organism to o·1 per cent, β-galactosidase synthesis can occur at about 25 per cent of the normal rate. An essentially similar result was obtained with the enzyme phosphatase.[15] Thus, these experiments involving the transfer of a radioactive chromosome, far from demonstrating the dependence of enzyme synthesis on the integrity of the chromosome, actually show that substantial synthesis of enzyme can continue after the radioactive decay of the chromosome has taken place; and they also show that this continued synthesis of enzyme is still susceptible to regulation by catabolite repression. The behaviour of bacteria in which the chromosome has been 'removed' by decay of radioactive phosphorus is thus not radically different from the behaviour of higher cells that have been enucleated. In both cases synthesis of specific proteins continues and can be regulated. The results of the isotope decay experiments are, of course, much less convincing than those obtained by direct enucleation in higher cells: we cannot be sure that the particular gene we are interested in has, in fact, been completely destroyed; and we do not know to what extent any secondary effect produced by the radiation might influence the physiological function we are examining. Indeed, some recent experiments with a radiation-sensitive strain of *E. coli* indicate that radioactive phosphorus decay in the chromosome has little effect on transcription of the DNA or on enzyme synthesis, but replication of the DNA and cell multiplication are severely impaired.[16]

(3) The argument based on the different effects produced in bacteria by the T-even phages on the one hand and λ phage on the other can also be dismissed. It has been shown that depolymerization of the bacterial DNA is a relatively late and secondary effect produced by infection with the T-even phages.[17] The synthetic processes of the bacterium can be inhibited by the T-even phages even when the bacterial DNA can be shown to be unimpaired. Moreover, non-infective 'ghosts' of phage T2 (shells of the phage not containing nucleic acid) are capable of inhibiting the synthesis of protein in the bacterium. The inhibition produced by phage ghosts involves no degradation of the bacterial DNA and is, in fact, reversible.[18] The mechanism by which the T-even phages inhibit protein synthesis in a susceptible bacterium remains unresolved, and

we cannot at present state definitely at what level the primary effect is exerted. It is, however, clear that the differences between phages that do grossly inhibit bacterial protein synthesis and those that do not, cannot be used to support the idea that integrity of the bacterial chromosome is essential for bacterial protein synthesis.

(4) We come finally to the very complex problem of the effects produced by 5-fluorouracil. Jacob and Monod state that the effects of 5-fluorouracil are virtually immediate and involve the production of homogeneously abnormal proteins. However, the experiment on alkaline phosphatase to which they refer[10] shows that, even under normal conditions, the induced synthesis of this enzyme is preceded by a prolonged lag period; and, in the presence of the analogue, this lag approaches 30 min which is close to one complete generation time for *E. coli*. In the case of β-galactosidase, induced synthesis of the enzyme did not occur at all in the presence of the analogue;[11] and all observations were therefore limited to a constitutive strain of *E. coli* in which synthesis of the enzyme was not completely abolished by 5-fluorouracil. In the presence of the analogue synthesis of β-galactosidase in this constitutive strain continued at about 20 per cent of the normal rate, but the cells produced in much larger amounts a protein (or proteins) that were enzymatically inactive but cross-reacted with antiserum against β-galactosidase. The assumption was made that the cross-reacting protein was an altered, enzymatically inactive, form of β-galactosidase induced by the action of the 5-fluorouracil. However, other interpretations are possible. It is known, for example, that even under normal conditions (that is, in the absence of 5-fluorouracil) large amounts of protein are formed in *E. coli* that are enzymatically inactive and cross-react with anti-β-galactosidase antiserum (the PZ proteins).[3] In the absence of more detailed characterization of the cross-reacting protein formed in the presence of 5-fluorouracil it is therefore impossible to say whether it is indeed an abortive form of the enzyme or whether it is something else altogether. A recent study of the effects of 5-fluorouracil on induced synthesis of β-galactosidase in *E. coli* has, in fact, shown that the inhibition of β-galactosidase synthesis is due, not to the formation of a false template, but to catabolite repression resulting from abnormal accumulation of

the intermediates of carbohydrate metabolism. Synthesis of perfectly normal enzyme occurs in the presence of 5-fluorouracil under conditions where this catabolite repression is relieved, even though the analogue is incorporated into RNA.[19] Other studies show that more than half the uracil in the RNA of growing bacteria can be replaced by 5-fluorouracil with very little metabolic disturbance: the cells divide more slowly, but the overall rate of protein synthesis remains proportional to the growth rate.[20, 21] It is, in any case, very difficult to draw firm conclusions about the mechanisms by which substances like 5-fluorouracil exert their effects. Whether changes in the behaviour of a particular enzyme are directly due to the incorporation of the analogue into its template, or whether they are indirect effects, cannot, in the present stage of our knowledge, be decided. Both β-galactosidase[22] and alkaline phosphatase[23] are polymeric enzymes that may exist in the cytoplasm of the cell in multiple molecular forms. Alterations in the temperature sensitivity or in other properties of these enzymes might be produced by essentially secondary changes in their physical state. A rich literature testifies to the complexity of the effects produced in cells by nucleic acid analogues.

3. Negative control, the operon, and the repressor

At the time that Jacob and Monod put forward their genetic operator model, the map of the genetic region concerned with the synthesis of β-galactosidase was thought to contain five components: three of these were apparently structural genes specifying β-galactosidase (z), galactoside permease (y), and galactoside transacetylase (a); and two, i and o, were elements concerned with regulation of the activity of the structural genes. Mutations at the i locus affected the inducibility of β-galactosidase synthesis by exogenous inducers; mutations at the o ('operator') locus affected the expression of the whole group of structural genes. Genetic mapping indicated that the order of the genes in this region was $i\ o\ z\ y\ a$. An additional genetic locus was later discovered that also appeared to regulate or facilitate transcription of the structural genes. This was named the p ('promoter') locus and appeared to map between o and z. The complete genetic map for this region was thus thought to be $i\ o\ p\ z\ y\ a$ in that order. This cluster of genes, all concerned with the synthesis of β-galactosidase, was called an 'operon' (the *lac* operon), a term that was soon widely used to describe any closely linked sequence of metabolically related genes that could be regulated co-ordinately as a single unit.

The idea that the expression of bacterial genes was controlled by the action of specific repressors arose initially from experiments involving sexual conjugation between strains of *E. coli* bearing mutations at the *i* locus. Wild type strains of *E. coli* normally synthesize β-galactosidase only when exposed to galactosides or certain other structurally related compounds. Such strains are said to be 'inducible' for β-galactosidase and are referred to as i^+. There are, however, mutations at the *i* locus that confer on the organism the ability to synthesize large amounts of β-galactosidase in the absence of exogenous inducers. These mutant strains are termed 'constitutive' and are referred to as i^-. When i^+ and i^- organisms were mated, it was found that the heterogenotes were i^+, that is, they did not synthesize β-galactosidase in the absence of an inducer.[24] Non-synthesis (inducibility) of the enzyme was thus found to be dominant over synthesis (constitutivity). Enzymes that show dominance of non-synthesis in this situation are commonly said to be under 'negative control'. In order to explain negative control, Jacob and Monod postulated that the product of the *i* gene was a specific repressor that inhibited the expression of the whole *lac* operon. Initially, the precise nature of this repressor was not specified; but, in due course, a more precise model was advanced in which it was proposed that the repressor was a protein that acted by virtue of its specific ability to bind to the *o* region of the operon and thus inhibit the transcription of the whole group of genes concerned with the synthesis of β-galactosidase.

Although a great deal of work was done on the genetics and physiology of the *lac* operon for several years after Jacob and Monod put forward their repressor model, none of this work identified a specific repressor or provided any direct evidence about its mode of action. In 1966, however, Gilbert and Müller-Hill,[25] using the technique of equilibrium dialysis, identified in extracts of i^+ *E. coli* traces of a protein that bound isopropyl-thiogalactoside, an inducer of β-galactosidase, with great affinity. This protein was partially purified and was found to attach, again with great affinity, to preparations of

PLATE 5

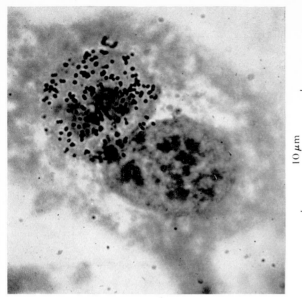

10 μm

b

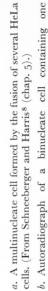

1 μm

a

a. A multinucleate cell formed by the fusion of several HeLa cells. (From Schneeberger and Harris[8] (chap. 5).)

b. Autoradiograph of a binucleate cell containing one HeLa nucleus and one Ehrlich nucleus. The HeLa cells had been grown in [3H] thymidine before the heterokaryons were produced. The HeLa nucleus is labelled and the Ehrlich nucleus is not. (From Harris[2] (chap. 5).)

PLATE 6

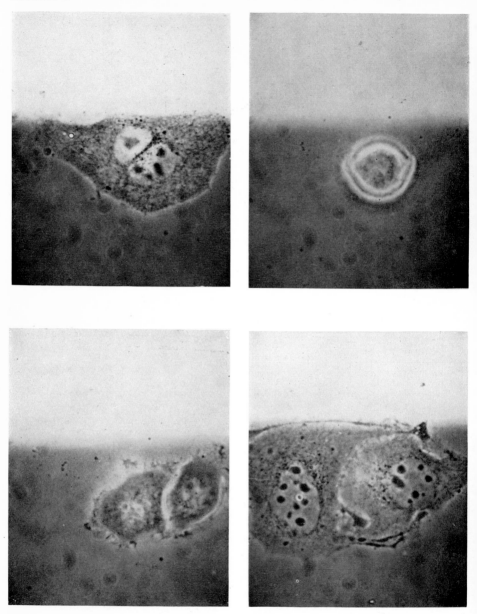

Four frames from a cinematographic sequence showing a HeLa-
Ehrlich heterokaryon undergoing mitosis and giving rise to two
hybrid mononucleate daughter cells.

PLATE 7

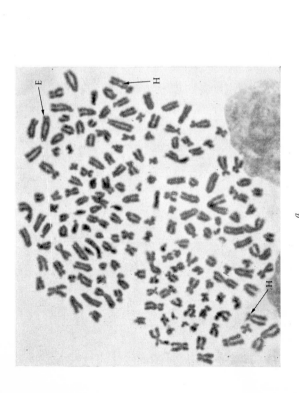

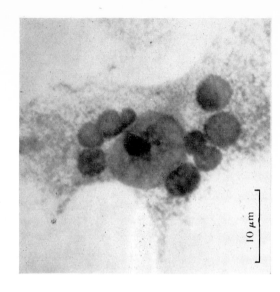

a

b

a. A HeLa-Ehrlich hybrid at metaphase. This cell contains 181 chromosomes in poroportions very close to those expected from the fusion of one modal Ehrlich cell and two modal HeLa cells. Arrows indicate two HeLa (H) and one Ehrlich (E) marker chromosomes. (From Harris *et al.*[5] (chap. 5).)

b. A heterokaryon containing one HeLa nucleus and a number of rabbit macrophage nuclei. (From Harris *et al.*[4] (chap. 5).)

PLATE 8

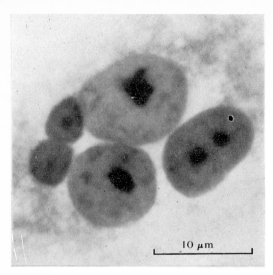

a. A heterokaryon containing three HeLa nuclei and two rat lymphocyte nuclei. (From Harris *et al.*[4] (chap. 5).)

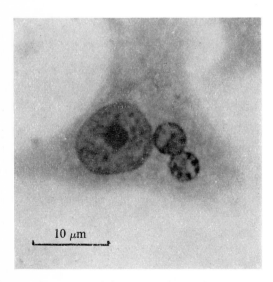

b. A heterokaryon containing one HeLa nucleus and two chick erythrocyte nuclei.

bacteriophage DNA that carried the *E. coli lac* genes, but not to preparations of bacteriophage DNA from which these genes were absent.[26] The affinity of this protein for the DNA of the *lac* region was strongly modified by mutations that appeared to map in the *o* region. These experiments thus demonstrated the existence of a protein, apparently specified by the *i* gene, that interacted both with exogenous inducer and with the *o* region of the *lac* operon. Gilbert and Müller-Hill concluded that this protein was the repressor predicted by Jacob and Monod, and that it acted, precisely as Jacob and Monod had suggested, by attaching specifically to the operator region of the *lac* DNA.

These experiments obviously provided strong evidence in favour of the genetic operator model, at least for the control of β-galactosidase synthesis in *E. coli*. There are, however, some difficulties. To begin with, a more detailed genetic analysis of the *lac* region has revealed that the order of the genes is not *i o p z y a*, but *i p o z y a*, that is, the promoter region (*p*), which appears to govern the rate of transcription of the whole *lac* operon, precedes the operator region (*o*).[27] Since transcription begins at or near *p*, the *o* region must therefore be transcribed. This means that each transcription product of the *lac* operon contains an RNA sequence homologous with the DNA of the *o* region. If this RNA sequence is translated, then the *o* locus must form part of the structural protein of β-galactosidase or of some other protein; but if, as some genetic evidence suggests, this RNA sequence is not normally translated, we are faced with the conclusion that each RNA template for the structural genes of the *lac* region begins with an untranslated region corresponding to the *o* locus. It is difficult to see what purpose this untranslated region could serve if it did not play some regulatory role in the translation of the template; and the possibility must be considered that the product of the *i* gene might, in the intact cell, interact with the *o* region of the RNA and thus exercise a control at the level of translation. It could be argued against this possibility, that the repressor protein studied by Gilbert and Müller-Hill binds only to double-stranded, and not to de-natured, single-stranded, DNA;[25] but denatured DNA is a highly disordered complex, whereas we can be sure that the RNA templates in the cytoplasm of the cell, although single-stranded, cannot be in a structurally disordered state, since they must, after all, be translated. Moreover, negative control, as revealed by the dominance of inducibility over constitutivity, is by no means the rule. The groups of enzymes involved in the utilization of maltose,[28] L-rhamnose,[29] and L-arabinose,[30] and in the reduction of sulphate,[31] in *E. coli* are under 'positive' control: constitutivity in these cases is dominant over inducibility. Indeed, even in the *lac* operon, i^- mutants have recently been described that show dominance of constitutivity. In order to explain this positive control for β-galactosidase in terms of repressor-operator interaction, complementation between the subunits of normal and mutant repressor has been invoked: it has been suggested that all combinations of normal and mutant subunits give rise to defective repressor, so that very little normal repressor is assembled if the mutant subunits are produced in excess.[32] The failure to assemble normal repressor would then account for the dominance of constitutivity. This explanation cannot, however, be generally applicable. In the case of the L-arabinose system, constitutivity may be dominant even with mutants in which the regulatory locus has been deleted, thus eliminating the possibility that the effect could be due to the production of defective repressor subunits.[33] It seems necessary to postulate, in at least some of these cases of positive control, that the regulatory genes function, not by specifying the synthesis of a repressor, but by stimulating or facilitating the expression of the structural genes in some way. Whether this facilitation operates at the level of transcription or translation is at present an open question. A further complication arises from more recent analysis of the phenomenon of catabolite repression. It has been shown that mutants of *E. coli* in which the *i, o,* and *p* loci have been deleted nonetheless show catabolite repression of β-galactosidase synthesis.[34] This finding demonstrates that regulation of the synthesis of β-galactosidase can be achieved without the intervention of the repressor-operator system; and since this regulation is effective when all the regulatory genetic loci of the *lac* region have been deleted, it seems probable that it operates at the level of translation.

   That translational regulatory mechanisms do operate in bacteria is certain. Perhaps the most decisive evidence comes from the study of RNA-containing bacteriophages. Each of these bacteriophages contains an RNA sequence that specifies the structure of three or four proteins; and when this sequence is translated in the bacterial cell, it can be shown that the proteins are synthesized in different amounts and at different times.[35-38] Moreover, these differential effects persist even when the bacteriophage RNA is translated *in vitro* in a disrupted cell system,[39] a situation that eliminates the possibility of regulation at any level other than translation. If these bacteriophages carry a 'polarity' mutation, the polarity is also expressed when the bacteriophage RNA is translated *in vitro*.[40] (A polarity mutation is one that not only affects the expression of the gene in which it occurs, but also reduces the activity of neighbouring genes.) The analysis of polarity mutations in the *lac* operon and in the operons governing the biosynthesis of tryptophan and histidine also reveals the intervention of translational regulatory mechanisms. In the case of the *lac* operon, it has been shown that the structural proteins are synthesized in different molar amounts and that these amounts may be varied relative to each other by changes in temperature.[41] An examination of polarity mutations affecting the z or the z and y genes of the *lac* operon has shown that the expression of the a gene depends upon the prior translation of the RNA produced by the y gene; and mutations in the z gene that result in premature cessation of the transcription of this gene do not inhibit the expression of the whole operon but permit polypeptide synthesis to be re-initiated at the beginning of the RNA sequence made by the y gene, or elsewhere.[42] When the expression of the tryptophan operon is inhibited by exogenous tryptophan, synthesis of the enzymes specified by the proximal genes in the operon quickly stops, but the enzymes specified by the more distal genes continue to be synthesized for as long as 13 min.[43] When the expression of the histidine operon is inhibited by exogenous histidine, the synthesis of the enzymes specified by the operon is suppressed in a temporal sequence that corresponds to the positional sequence of the genes; but when the first enzyme in the sequence undergoes a mutation that renders it insensitive to normal feed-back inhibition, exogenous histidine then suppresses the synthesis of all the enzymes simultaneously.[44] These polarity effects in the *lac*, tryptophan, and histidine operons so closely resemble those described in the RNA bacteriophages that it is difficult to believe that they do not involve the same kinds of regulatory mechanisms. It is, in any case, clear that these effects cannot be explained by transcriptional controls alone. While most people now believe, in the light of the experiments of Gilbert and Müller-Hill, that in *E. coli* the induction of β-galactosidase by galactosides does involve a transcriptional control element, it is difficult to avoid the conclusion that any such transcriptional controls must operate against a background of more general and more flexible translational regulatory mechanisms. There are therefore no good grounds for entertaining the notion that protein synthesis in bacteria is regulated predominantly by mechanisms operating at the genetic level, while that in higher cells is regulated predominantly by cytoplasmic mechanisms. Cytoplasmic regulatory mechanisms are obviously fundamental to both forms of organization. In bacteria, it seems possible that certain specialized forms of transcriptional control may have been evolved in response to the requirement for rapid adaptation to qualitative changes in nutrient supply. The cells of higher animals and plants are not normally subjected to dramatic alterations in nutrient supply, and, compared with bacteria, only small and very gradual changes in enzyme level can be induced in them. Transcriptional controls have nonetheless evolved in higher cells; but, as I shall discuss later, they bear little resemblance to the repressor circuitry that has been proposed for bacteria.

4. The stability of the templates in bacteria

One of the most important conclusions that the genetic operator model entailed, and one properly emphasized by Jacob and Monod, was that the templates for the synthesis of proteins had to be short-lived. If the synthesis of proteins was to be regulated *only* by mechanisms that intervened at the level of DNA transcription, the RNA templates would have to be rapidly destroyed: if they were not, switching off the relevant gene would not switch off the synthesis of the corresponding protein. This corollary of the genetic operator model is, once again, directly at variance with the observations on animal and plant cells. As we have seen, enucleation studies on eukaryotic cells indicate a very high degree of stability of the templates for protein synthesis: their life span may be as long as several months and, even in the least favourable case, cannot be less than several hours. And it must again be emphasized that all these estimates are minimum estimates. Synthesis of protein as a whole or synthesis of any particular protein may run down in an enucleate cell for reasons that have nothing to do with destruction of templates. While persistence of synthesis does indicate that the template is still intact, cessation of synthesis does not necessarily indicate that the template has been destroyed. If it should prove that the templates for protein synthesis in bacteria are indeed short-lived, while those in higher cells are not, this would be another generalization of great importance, for it would mean either that there are fundamental differences in structure between the templates of higher cells and those of bacteria, or that there are fundamental differences in the enzymatic machinery that destroys the templates.

Before any serious discussion of the life span of templates can be undertaken, some precision must be given to the terms 'short-lived' or 'long-lived'. The lifetime of a template could, of course, be expressed in absolute terms: so many minutes, so many hours, or so many days. But this is not a very informative parameter; since the life cycle of different cells shows such great variation. The generation time of *E. coli* under optimal conditions might be about 30 min, the generation time of animal cells growing *in vitro* might be as low as 8 to 10 h, the normal life span of *Acetabularia mediterranea* is about 3 months, and the human small lymphocyte may survive without multiplication for 15 years or more. In terms of the generation time of the cell, 3 min in *E. coli* might be equivalent to 1 h in a tissue culture cell and 10 days in *Acetabularia*. Variations in the life span of the templates for protein synthesis in these different organisms might thus simply reflect the more leisurely operation of the regulatory mechanisms in more slowly growing cells. Such variations do not necessarily imply that different kinds of regulatory mechanisms are operative. The point of substance is whether suppression of the synthesis of a particular protein involves the destruction of its template as a *necessary* part of the mechanism. The genetic operator model postulates that the synthesis of the protein stops because the template is destroyed; and since the model requires the lifetime of the template to be short relative to the generation time of the cells, templates must continually be replaced at a rate much faster than that required simply by the growth of the organism. The crucial question is therefore whether the lifetime of the template is, or is not, longer than the time required to suppress the synthesis of the particular protein that one is studying. If, for example, the synthesis of β-galactosidase is suppressed within 2 or 3 min by the removal of an inducer or by the provision of an alternative source of metabolizable carbohydrate, then the genetic operator model insists that the life of the templates for β-galactosidase cannot be longer than 2–3 min. We know that this model cannot account for the regulation of enzyme synthesis in higher cells, because the regulatory mechanisms in these cells operate perfectly well on templates that remain intact for long periods after removal of the nucleus. The point at issue is, then, whether rapid destruction of the templates forms an essential part of the regulatory mechanisms that govern enzyme synthesis in bacteria.

The essential weakness of bacteria as experimental material for the elucidation of this sort of problem is the fact that they do not possess a clearly bounded nucleus and hence cannot be enucleated. All experiments of this kind in bacteria have had to rely on the use of indirect forms of 'physiological enucleation' produced either by radioactive decay in the chromosome or by high concentrations of actinomycin D. While only a few investigations in bacteria have exploited isotope decay as a means of studying regulatory mechanisms, there is a rich literature based on the use of actinomycin D. It goes without saying that it is a confused literature, since actinomycin D does less than enucleation in one respect (in eliminating the direct intervention of the genes) and a great deal more in another (in producing severe and complex secondary effects). I think no very useful purpose would be served in attempting a detailed survey of the estimates that have been made of the life span of templates for different proteins from measurements of the fall in the rate of synthesis of these proteins in the presence of actinomycin D. The estimates range from 2 to 3 min (for the β-galactosidase of *E. coli*)[45] to periods that may approach or even exceed the generation time of the bacterium involved.[46] They vary from one type of organism to another, and, even in the one organism, they may be influenced by the cultural conditions used.[47] The kinetics of the decay of protein synthesis in the presence of actinomycin D are also extremely variable: in some cases the decay curves suggest a simply exponential function;[48] in others they are composed of at least two, but probably many more, different exponentials;[49] and in others again they have a 'multi-hit' character suggesting that more than one event is required to produce a perceptible effect.[50] The onset of the decay is always preceded by a lag period, and this, too, varies greatly in duration. I am afraid that I shall continue to find it very difficult to entertain any of these observations as serious estimates of the life span of RNA templates, until some convincing evidence is provided that the decay in the rate of protein synthesis is in fact determined by the destruction of the templates, and by this alone.

5. Templates with different stabilities

The wide variations that have been observed in the rate of decay of protein synthesis in the presence of actinomycin D have given rise to a modification of the genetic operator model that merits some consideration. Whereas the original model proposed by Jacob and Monod stipulated that all the templates for the synthesis of protein must be short-lived, it has more recently been suggested that the templates may differ in their stability, and that their differences in this respect may impart flexibility to the regulatory mechanisms that govern the synthesis of the corresponding proteins.[51] It has been proposed that enzymes whose rate of synthesis is subject to rapid change, as, for example, the β-galactosidase in inducible strains of E. coli, have short-lived templates; whereas enzymes whose rate of synthesis changes more slowly, for example, the penicillinase of B. cereus, have templates with a longer life span. The argument is that these differences in life span are reflected by the differences in the rates at which the synthesis of these proteins decays in the presence of actinomycin D. A special case of this general proposition is the idea that the templates for a particular enzyme would be short-lived in organisms in which the enzyme is inducible and long-lived in organisms in which it is produced constitutively. This model still assumes that the regulatory mechanisms governing the synthesis of the proteins operate essentially via transcription of the DNA, but it adds the notion that the immediacy, and hence the flexibility, of the control is governed by the life span of the template.

It is at present very difficult to test this model experimentally. In only very few cases, where unusually favourable genetic circumstances have permitted a plausible application of the technique of DNA-RNA hybridization, has it been possible to identify with any degree of assurance the template for a particular protein;[52] but, even in these cases, direct measurement of the life span of the template is fraught with difficulty. Why this should be so will become apparent in a later chapter when the kinetics of RNA turnover are discussed. However, there are reasons which, in my view, make it difficult to believe that variations in the life span of RNA templates form an essential part of the regulatory mechanisms that govern the synthesis of proteins. If one imagines that the templates for protein synthesis vary widely in their stability, one is immediately faced with the problem of explaining how this variability is achieved. There seem to me to be three possible ways in which this could be done: (1) there might be structural differences between templates that determine their susceptibility to hydrolysis by cytoplasmic degradative enzymes; (2) there might be specific degradative enzymes for different classes of templates, and these enzymes could operate at very different rates; and (3) the templates might be shielded from the degradative enzymes, but the degree of shielding could vary. None of these alternatives seems to me to be at all attractive. What we know about the relationship between the structure of ribonucleic acids and their susceptibility to ribonucleases does not encourage the hope that subtle differences in base sequence would permit great variations in resistance to degradation. As far as we know at present, double strandedness, absence of pyrimidines or of one of the purines, methylation of the sugar, and the nature of the end groups are the only intrinsic factors that can substantially affect the resistance of polyribonucleotides to degradation by nucleases. Since all active templates must, in any case, function as templates, it seems unlikely that they would show gross differences in their degree of secondary structure. Absence of pyrimidines or of one of the purines cannot be a feature of natural ribonucleic acids; nor can all their sugar residues be methylated. One might imagine protective base sequences at the ends of some of the templates, but, in the cell, the templates might well have to contend with both exonucleases and endonucleases with different specificity requirements. Differences in template structure could not, in any event, explain the proposed difference in stability between the templates of constitutive and inducible forms of the same enzyme: here the templates must be structurally identical.

The second possibility requires a much larger number of degradative enzymes than are known to exist, and also enzymes with a much greater degree of specificity. But even if large numbers of highly specific degradative enzymes proved eventually to be forthcoming, this scheme would also fail to account for the proposed difference in stability between the templates of constitutive and inducible forms of the same enzyme.

There is good evidence that templates that are being translated are, in some way, shielded from degradation;[53, 54] but this form of shielding involves no specificity, and it implies that the templates that are actually supporting the synthesis of protein do not have a short life. Any model that requires specificity of shielding must propose either that there are different shields for different templates or that there are varying degrees of closeness of fit between the shield and the template. The first alternative again entails an array of highly specific and hitherto undiscovered proteins; the second implies major differences in the secondary or tertiary structure of the templates. Variable shielding of the templates is too vague a proposition to permit serious analysis, but, to my mind, it gives rise to greater conceptual difficulties than those that it is designed to resolve. There is no doubt that, under certain conditions, RNA templates can be degraded in the cell; and the templates in one part of the cell may well be degraded more readily than those in another. But more plausible mechanisms will need to be proposed than those that I have been able to envisage, before much enthusiasm can be generated for the idea that variations in the stability of templates provide a general mechanism for regulating the synthesis of proteins.

6. Comparisons between bacteria and eukaryotic cells

The term 'operon' implies that the functional significance of clustering of related genes is to be explained in terms of co-ordinate regulation of the corresponding enzymes. This is rather unlikely. Sequences of metabolically related enzymes may be regulated co-ordinately whether the corresponding genes show close linkage or not. This is true not only for higher cells, in which clustering of metabolically related genes may be the exception rather than the rule, but also for bacteria. Even in *E. coli*, genes specifying a sequence of related enzymes may be clustered as in the *lac* region, dispersed as in the case of the enzymes mediating proline biosynthesis,[55] or partly clustered and partly dispersed as in the case of the enzymes mediating arginine biosynthesis.[56, 57] Yet all these enzyme sequences are regulated co-ordinately without difficulty. It is thus obvious that gene clustering cannot be a prerequisite for co-ordinate regulation. An alternative possibility is that gene clustering might facilitate the assembly of related proteins where these normally function together as a multi-enzyme complex; but not all sequences of metabolically related enzymes form such structural complexes. Another possibility is that gene clustering may provide a selective advantage for organisms in which sexual conjugation is achieved by the passage of a single chromosome from one cell to another. This form of sexuality, which is characteristic of bacteria, involves a high risk that the chromosome might break during the act of conjugation. It might be an advantage to minimize the incidence of breaks that would result in the delivery of an incomplete set of metabolically related genes to the recipient cell, and clustering of such genes would obviously achieve this end. One would then expect to find gene clustering much less frequently in organisms that do not exhibit this form of sexuality; and this does appear to be the case. It is, in any case, clear that the biological significance of gene clustering is more complex than is implied by the term 'operon', and it is likely that we shall find a more satisfactory explanation for this phenomenon in evolutionary terms than in terms of metabolic regulation.

In attempting to assess how far bacteria differ from higher cells in their mechanisms for regulating protein synthesis, it would obviously be a great advantage if one could compare the same metabolic event in the two situations. This is by no means easy. By far the most detailed studies on the regulation of protein synthesis in bacteria have been carried out on rapid changes induced in a sequence of related enzymes represented genetically by a cluster of closely linked genes. Events of this sort may be without parallel in the cells of higher animals or plants. In the latter, even modest changes in the levels of the common metabolic enzymes require the passage of several hours or even days; and the genes specifying related sequences of enzymes are not, in general, closely linked. It is difficult in higher cells to find an event that is closely analogous to the induction of β-galactosidase in *E. coli*. There are, however, two highly regulated processes that do take place in both bacteria and eukaryotic cells and have been extensively studied in both situations: sporulation and germination. Spores, or biologically equivalent bodies, are formed under appropriate conditions by a wide range of plants, and the over-all pattern of sporulation in these eukaryotic organisms is essentially similar to that seen in bacteria. In both cases an elaborate programme of biochemical and morphological changes results in the production of cells encased in materials that are highly resistant to inclement changes in the environment and ensure the survival of the cell until conditions propitious for growth are again established. The development of the cap in *Acetabularia*, which permits the formation and release of cysts containing the gametes, and the development of fruiting bodies in certain myxomycetes are essentially analogous processes. I have already discussed in some detail the experiments that have been done on *Acetabularia* cells from which the nucleus has been removed. These experiments have established that the whole intricate process of cap formation does not require the concomitant presence of the cell nucleus. All the information required for the development of the cap passes to the cytoplasm of the cell long before it is expressed; and the biochemical changes that result in cap formation are elaborated by cytoplasmic regulatory mechanisms that operate perfectly well in the absence of the relevant genes. Essentially the same principles appear to hold for the formation of the fruiting body in the slime mould *Dictyostelium*; and they also appear to hold for the formation of spores in bacteria. In neither of the latter cases is enucleation possible, but the results obtained by the use of actinomycin D leave little doubt that the over-all organization of these two processes is achieved in the same way as the formation of the cap in *Acetabularia*. In both

cases proteins associated specifically with the progressive morphological differentiation are synthesized many hours after
RNA synthesis has been largely inhibited by high doses of
actinomycin D;[58-64] and detailed analysis of the patterns of
response to this antibiotic indicates that the information for any
particular event in the sporulation or fruiting process is
delivered to the cytoplasm of the cell long before that event
actually takes place.[64-66] In bacteria, as in eukaryotic cells, the
translation of the templates that govern sporulation is initiated
and regulated by processes that are far removed in time from
those that determine the transcription of the corresponding
genes. The same holds true for the process of germination during
which the spore, cyst, or seed resumes vegetative growth.
Germination in wheat embryos induces a wave of protein synthesis that may continue for as long as 24 hours without appreciable RNA synthesis;[67] and observations on the effects of
actinomycin D on the germination of the microcysts of the
fruiting myxobacterium *Myxococcus xanthus* indicate that here,
too, the information necessary for germination is delivered to
the cytoplasm of the cell at least 4 or 5 hours before it is
expressed.[68]

It thus appears that in two fundamental biological processes
that bacteria share with higher cells, the over-all pattern of
organization, not only in the higher cells, but also in the
bacteria, follows the general principles that have been derived
from the study of *Acetabularia*. During sporulation and germination there is no close coupling, either in bacteria or in higher
cells, between the time at which a gene is transcribed and the
time at which the corresponding template is translated into
protein. The mechanisms that initiate the synthesis of the
proteins specific for these two forms of differentiation, and
that regulate their subsequent production, are located in the
cytoplasm of the cell and do not operate by governing the
transcription of the DNA.

REFERENCES

1. JACOB, F. and MONOD, J. (1961). Genetic regulatory mechanisms in
   the synthesis of proteins. *J. molec. Biol.* **3**, 318.
2. PARDEE, A. B. and PRESTIDGE, L. S. (1961). The initial kinetics of
   enzyme induction. *Biochim. biophys. Acta* **49**, 77.

3. COHN, M. (1957). Contributions of studies on the β-galactosidase of Escherichia coli to our understanding of enzyme synthesis. Bact. Rev. **21**, 140.

4. RILEY, M., PARDEE, A. B., JACOB, F., and MONOD, J. (1960). On the expression of a structural gene. J. molec. Biol. **2**, 216.

5. COHEN, S. S. (1949). Growth requirements of bacterial viruses. Bact. Rev. **13**, 1.

6. MONOD, J. and WOLLMAN, E. (1947). L'inhibition de la croissance et de l'adaptation enzymatique chez les bactéries infectées par le bactériophage. Annls Inst. Pasteur, Paris **73**, 937.

7. BENZER, S. (1953). Induced synthesis of enzymes in bacteria analyzed at the cellular level. Biochim. biophys. Acta **11**, 383.

8. LURIA, S. E. and HUMAN, M. L. (1950). Chromatin staining of bacteria during bacteriophage infection. J. Bact. **59**, 551.

9. SIMINOVITCH, L. and JACOB, F. (1952). Biosynthèse induite d'un enzyme pendant le développement des bactériophages chez Escherichia coli K12. Annls Inst. Pasteur, Paris **83**, 745.

10. NAONO, S. and GROS, F. (1960). Synthèse par E. coli d'une phosphatase modifiée en présence d'un analogue pyrimidique. C. r. hebd. Séanc. Acad. Sci., Paris **250**, 3889.

11. BUSSARD, B., NAONO, S., GROS, F., and MONOD, J. (1960). Effets d'un analogue de l'uracile sur les propriétés d'une protéine enzymatique synthétisée en sa présence. C. r. hebd. Séanc. Acad. Sci., Paris **250**, 4049.

12. BRAMWELL, M. E. and HARRIS, H. (1967). The origin of the polydispersity in sedimentation patterns of rapidly labelled nuclear RNA. Biochem. J. **103**, 816.

13. SEDAT, J., LYON, A., and SINSHEIMER, R. L. (1969). Purification of Escherichia coli pulse-labelled RNA by benzoylated DEAE-cellulose chromatography. J. molec. Biol. **44**, 415.

14. SILVER, S. D. (1963). The transfer of material during mating in Escherichia coli. Transfer of DNA and upper limits on the transfer of RNA and protein. J. molec. Biol. **6**, 349.

15. McFALL, E. (1961). Effects of ^{32}P decay on enzyme synthesis. J. molec. Biol. **3**, 219.

16. DAVERN, C. I. (1968). Effect of ^{32}P decay upon RNA transcription by a radiation-sensitive strain of Escherichia coli. J. molec. Biol. **32**, 151.

17. NOMURA, M., MATSUBARA, K., OKAMOTO, K., and FUJIMURA, R. (1962). Inhibition of host nucleic acid and protein synthesis by bacteriophage T4: its relation to the physical and functional integrity of host chromosome. J. molec. Biol. **5**, 535.

18. FRENCH, R. C. and SIMINOVITCH, L. (1954). The action of T2 bacteriophage ghosts on Escherichia coli B. Can. J. Microbiol. **1**, 757.

19. HOROWITZ, J. and KOHLMEIER, V. (1967). Formation of active β-galactosidase by Escherichia coli treated with 5-fluorouracil. Biochim. biophys. Acta **142**, 208.

20. SAUNDERS, P. P., BASS, R. E., and SAUNDERS, G. I. (1968). Properties of 5-fluorouracil-containing ribonucleic acid and ribosomes from Bacillus subtilis. J. Bact. **96**, 525.

21. SAUNDERS, P. P., SCHULTZ, G. A., and SAUNDERS, G. I. (1968). Effect of 5-fluorouracil on the growth and morphology of a polyauxotrophic strain of *Bacillus subtilis*. *J. Bact.* **96,** 560.
22. APPEL, S. H., ALPERS, D. H., and TOMKINS, G. M. (1965). Multiple molecular forms of β-galactosidase. *J. molec. Biol.* **11,** 12.
23. LEVINTHAL, C., SIGNER, E. R., and FETHEROLF, K. (1962). Reactivation and hybridization of reduced alkaline phosphatase. *Proc. natn. Acad. Sci. U.S.A.* **48,** 1230.
24. JACOB, F. and MONOD, J. (1961). On the regulation of gene activity. *Cold Spring Harb. Symp. quant. Biol.* **26,** 193.
25. GILBERT, W. and MÜLLER-HILL, B. (1966). Isolation of the lac repressor. *Proc. natn. Acad. Sci. U.S.A.* **56,** 1891.
26. GILBERT, W. and MÜLLER-HILL, B. (1967). The lac operator is DNA. *Proc. natn. Acad. Sci. U.S.A.* **58,** 2415.
27. IPPEN, K., MILLER, J. H., SCAIFE, J., and BECKWITH, J. (1968). A new controlling element in the *lac* operon of *E. coli*. *Nature, Lond.* **217,** 825.
28. HATFIELD, D., HOFNUNG, M., and SCHWARTZ, M. (1969). Genetic analysis of the maltose A region in *Escherichia coli*. *J. Bact.* **98,** 559.
29. POWER, J. (1967). The L-rhamnose genetic system in *Escherichia coli* K-12. *Genetics* **55,** 557.
30. ENGELSBERG, E., IRR, J., POWER, J., and LEE, N. (1965). Positive control of enzyme synthesis by gene *C* in the L-arabinose system. *J. Bact.* **90,** 946.
31. JONES-MORTIMER, M. C. (1968). Positive control of sulphate reduction in *Escherichia coli*. *Biochem. J.* **110,** 589 and 597.
32. MÜLLER-HILL, B., CRAPO, L., and GILBERT, W. (1968). Mutants that make more lac repressor. *Proc. natn. Acad. Sci. U.S.A.* **59,** 1259.
33. ENGELSBERG, E., SHEPPARD, D., SQUIRES, C., and MERONK, F. (1969). An analysis of "revertants" of a deletion mutant in the *C* gene of the L-arabinose gene complex in *Escherichia coli* B/r: isolation of initiator constitutive mutants (I°). *J. molec. Biol.* **43,** 281.
34. MOSES, V. and YUDKIN, M. D. (1968). Catabolite repression in *Escherichia coli*. *Biochem. J.* **110,** 135.
35. OESCHGER, M. P. and NATHANS, D. (1966). Differential synthesis of bacteriophage-specific proteins in MS2-infected *Escherichia coli* treated with actinomycin. *J. molec. Biol.* **22,** 235.
36. NATHANS, D., OESCHGER, M. P., EGGEN, K., and SHIMURA, Y. (1966). Bacteriophage-specific proteins in *E. coli* infected with an RNA bacteriophage. *Proc. natn. Acad. Sci. U.S.A.* **56,** 1844.
37. LODISH, H. F. (1968). Bacteriophage f2 RNA: control of translation and gene order. *Nature, Lond.* **220,** 345.
38. LODISH, H. F. (1968). Independent translation of the genes of bacteriophage f2 RNA. *J. molec. Biol.* **32,** 681.
39. EGGEN, K., OESCHGER, M. P., and NATHANS, D. (1967). Cell-free protein synthesis directed by coliphage MS2 RNA: sequential synthesis of specific phage proteins. *Biochem. biophys. Res. Commun.* **28,** 587.
40. CAPECCHI, M. R. (1967). Polarity *in vitro*. *J. molec. Biol.* **30,** 213.

41. ZABIN, I. (1963). Proteins of the lactose system. *Cold Spring Harb. Symp. quant. Biol.* **28,** 431.

42. NEWTON, A. (1969). Re-initiation of polypeptide synthesis and polarity in the lac operon of *Escherichia coli. J. molec. Biol* **41,** 329.

43. ITO, J. and IMAMOTO, F. (1968). Sequential derepression and repression of the tryptophan operon in *E. Coli. Nature, Lond.* **220,** 441.

44. KOVACH, J. S. BERBERICH, M. A., VENETIANER, P., and GOLDBERGER, R. F. (1969). Repression of the histidine operon: effect of the first enzyme on the kinetics of repression. *J. Bact.* **97,** 1283.

45. LEIVE, L. (1965). Some effects of inducer on synthesis and utilization of β-galactosidase messenger RNA in actinomycin-sensitive *Escherichia coli. Biochem. biophys. Res. Commun.* **20,** 13.

46. POLLOCK, M. R. (1963). The differential effect of actinomycin D on the biosynthesis of enzymes in *Bacillus subtilis* and *Bacillus cereus. Biochim biophys. Acta* **76,** 80.

47. YUDKIN, M. D. (1965). Amino acid incorporation in *Bacillus megaterium* treated with actinomycin. *Biochim. biophys. Acta* **103,** 705.

48. LEVINTHAL, C., KEYNAN, A., and HIGA, A. (1962). Messenger RNA turnover and protein synthesis in *B. subtilis* inhibited by actinomycin D. *Proc. natn. Acad. Sci. U.S.A.* **48,** 1631.

49. FAN, D. P., HIGA, A., and LEVINTHAL, C. (1964). Messenger RNA decay and protection. *J. molec. Biol.* **8,** 210.

50. HARRIS, H. (1964). Function of the short-lived ribonucleic acid in the cell nucleus. *Nature, Lond.* **201,** 863.

51. MOSES, V. and CALVIN, M. (1965). Molecular regulation and its possible evolutionary significance. *Evolving genes and proteins* (Eds. V. BRYSON and H. J. VOGEL), p. 511, Academic Press, New York.

52. MCCARTHY, B. J. (1970). The specificity of molecular hybridization reactions. *A. Rev. Biochem.* In press.

53. BARONDES, S. H. and NIRENBERG, M. W. (1962). Fate of a synthetic polynucleotide directing cell-free protein synthesis. I. Characteristics of degradation. *Science, N.Y.* **138,** 810.

54. TAKANAMI, M. and ZUBAY, G. (1964). An estimate of the size of the ribosomal site for messenger RNA binding. *Proc. natn. Acad. Sci. U.S.A.* **51,** 834.

55. CURTISS, R. (1965). Chromosomal aberrations associated with mutations to bacteriophage resistance in *Escherichia coli. J. Bact.* **89,** 28.

56. VOGEL, H. J. (1953). Path of ornithine synthesis in *Escherichia coli. Proc. natn. Acad. Sci. U.S.A.* **39,** 578.

57. VOGEL, H. J. and BACON, D. F. (1966). Gene aggregation: evidence for a coming together of functionally related, not closely linked genes. *Proc. natn. Acad. Sci. U.S.A.* **55,** 1456.

58. SUSSMAN, M. and SUSSMAN, R. R. (1965). The regulatory program for UDP galactose polysaccharide transferase activity during slime mold cytodifferentiation: requirement for specific synthesis of ribonucleic acid. *Biochim. biophys. Acta* **108,** 463.

59. ROTH, R., ASHWORTH, J. M., and SUSSMAN, M. (1968). Periods of genetic transcription required for the synthesis of three enzymes

during cellular slime mold development. *Proc. natn. Acad. Sci. U.S.A.*
59, 1235.
60. NEWELL, P. C. and SUSSMAN, M. (1969). Uridine diphosphate glucose
pyrophosphorylase in *Dictyostelium discoideum.* Stability and developmental fate. *J. biol. Chem.* **244,** 2990.
61. ROSAS DEL VALLE, M. and ARONSON, A. I. (1962). Evidence for the
synthesis of stable informational RNA required for bacterial spore
formation. *Biochem. biophys. Res. Commun.* **9,** 421.
62. ARONSON, A. I. and ROSAS DEL VALLE, M. (1964). RNA and protein
synthesis required for bacterial spore formation. *Biochim. biophys. Acta*
87, 267.
63. MANDELSTAM, J. and STERLINI, J. M. (1969). "Commitment" to sporulation in *Bacillus subtilis. Spores IV,* p. 180. American Society for Microbiology.
64. LOOMIS, W. F. (1969). Developmental regulation of alkaline phosphatase in *Dictyostelium discoideum. J. Bact.* **100,** 417.
65. SUSSMAN, M. and SUSSMAN, R. (1969). Patterns of RNA synthesis and of
enzyme accumulation and disappearance during cellular slime mold
cytodifferentiation. *Symposia of the Society for General Microbiology,* XIX,
p. 403.
66. MANDELSTAM, J. (1969). Regulation of bacterial spore formation.
Symposia of the Society for General Microbiology, XIX, p. 377.
67. CHEN, D., SARID, S., and KATCHALSKI, E. (1968). Studies on the nature
of messenger RNA in germinating wheat embryos. *Proc. natn. Acad.
Sci. U.S.A.* **60,** 902.
68. SCOTT RAMSEY, W. and DWORKIN, M. (1970). Stable mRNA and
germination of *Myxococcus xanthus* microcysts. *J. Bact.* **101,** 531.

3. The search for the messenger

1. The background

LET me begin by defining what is now common ground in all discussions about transfer of information from the genes to the cytoplasm of the cell. Nobody, I think, disputes that the vehicle for this transfer is RNA; or that the DNA of the genes forms the template on which this RNA is synthesized; or that this RNA is released from the DNA and passes in some form to the cytoplasm of the cell where it acts as a template for the synthesis of proteins. If we limit the use of the word 'messenger' to RNA that has all three of these properties, I do not expect that much misunderstanding will arise. But RNA may be synthesized on the DNA in the cell nucleus without passing to the cytoplasm; RNA may be synthesized on this DNA and pass to the cytoplasm of the cell, but it may not be a template for the synthesis of proteins; and RNA may act as a template for protein synthesis in the cell cytoplasm, but it may not have been synthesized on the DNA in the cell nucleus. To use the term 'messenger' simply to designate any RNA, whatever its origin, that can act as a template for protein synthesis, saps the word 'messenger' of its normal meaning and introduces assumptions about the nature of the template which are tendentious, which may be wrong, and which, in any case, have given rise to great confusion.

Prior to the paper by Jacob and Monod[1] discussed in Chapter 2, there was no great controversy about which RNA in the cytoplasm acted as the template for protein synthesis. It was generally assumed, although no specific experiments were done to test the idea, that the specifications for the synthesis of proteins resided in the RNA of the ribosomes. These particles contain 85 per cent or more of the RNA in the cell cytoplasm, and it was therefore natural to assume that the bulk of the cyto-plasmic RNA would be fulfilling the only role that at that time could be envisaged for it, namely to serve as a template for protein synthesis.

The ideas of Jacob and Monod changed all that. Their genetic operator model required that the templates for protein synthesis should be short-lived. But there was ample evidence that the ribosomal RNA in the cytoplasm of the cell was not short-lived. Several studies on both bacterial and animal cells had shown that the bulk of the cellular RNA was not involved in rapid turnover;[2-4] and the experiments of Davern and Meselson,[5] in which density gradient centrifugation was used to measure changes in the density of RNA that had been labelled with heavy nitrogen, made it clear that, during ex-ponential growth, almost all the RNA in the bacterial cell was essentially stable. Ribosomal RNA could not therefore be the template envisaged by Jacob and Monod. Two other con-siderations cast doubt upon the assumption that the ribosomal ribonucleic acid acted as the template for protein synthesis; the apparent homogeneity of its base composition and of its molecular weight. It was supposed that, since the RNA tem-plates were synthesized on the DNA of the cell, their over-all base composition should resemble that of the DNA.[1] But it had been shown that, although the base composition of the DNA in bacteria differed widely, the overall base composition of the RNA was relatively constant: in almost all cases the RNA had a high cytidylic and guanylic acid content.[6] In animal and plant cells too, it was known that the ribosomal RNA showed little variation in base composition: it also had a high cytidylic and guanylic acid content, whereas the DNA in most higher cells had a high adenylic and uridylic acid content.[7, 8] Moreover, in the ultracentrifuge, ribosomal RNA separated as two discrete components, whereas if it were to serve as a template for the synthesis of a whole range of cellular proteins, one might expect much greater heterogeneity in its sedimentation behaviour. And so it was that, almost immediately, the theory put forward by Jacob and Monod initiated a search for other families of RNA molecules having the characteristics that the genetic operator model predicted that the 'messenger' should have.

2. The reported discovery of the 'messenger' and some doubts about the evidence

Even before the paper by Jacob and Monod was published (June 1961) two communications appeared together in the same issue of *Nature* (May 1961) claiming that the desired messenger had been found. One, by Brenner, Jacob, and Meselson,[9] was entitled 'An unstable intermediate carrying information from genes to ribosomes for protein synthesis'; the other, by Gros, Hiatt, Gilbert, Kurland, Risebrough, and Watson,[10] was entitled 'Unstable ribonucleic acid revealed by pulse labelling of *Escherichia coli*'. These two papers appeared to provide experimental verification of the genetic operator model, and thus did much to win widespread acceptance for it. The paper by Brenner *et al.* deals with the synthesis of RNA in *E. coli* infected with phage T4; that by Gros *et al.* extends the investigation to uninfected *E. coli* cells.

The essential findings in the paper by Gros *et al.* were as follows: (1) When *E. coli* cells were exposed for a very short time to [^{32}P]phosphate or [^{14}C]uracil (10–20 s at 25°C) the radioactivity was largely incorporated into an RNA fraction that differed in its sedimentation characteristics from the main ribosomal RNA components. In sucrose density gradients, under the particular experimental conditions used, the 'pulse-labelled' RNA sedimented as a very heterogeneous peak that varied in position between 8S and a little less than 16S; whereas the ribosomal RNA sedimented as two relatively homogeneous components with sedimentation coefficients of 23S and 16S (Fig. 4). (2) At higher concentrations of magnesium (up to 10^{-2}M) increasing amounts of this RNA were found to sediment in the position normally occupied by the 70S ribosomes. (3) When the pulse-labelled cells were transferred to non-radioactive medium, radioactivity disappeared from the heterogeneous component and appeared in the ribosomal RNA. From these findings the following conclusions were drawn: (1) that the pulse-labelling revealed a special class of RNA that was not ribosomal RNA or a precursor of ribosomal RNA; (2) that this RNA became attached to ribosomes at high concentrations of magnesium; and (3) that this RNA was 'metabolically unstable', that is to say, it was not only rapidly synthesized but also rapidly broken down. Were these conclusions justified, and how far has later work supported them?

It can be stated at the outset that no evidence was presented in this paper to support the conclusion that the pulse-labelled RNA was unstable. The passage of radioactivity from the pulse-labelled RNA to the ribosomal RNA was perfectly consistent

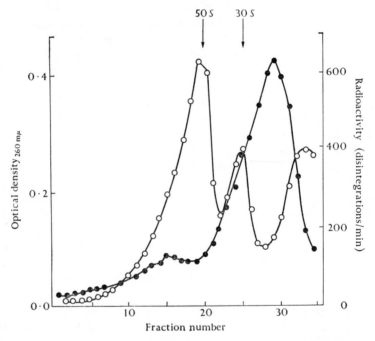

FIG. 4. Sucrose-density-gradient sedimentation pattern of a crude extract of *Escherichia coli* cells exposed to [14C]uracil for 20 s. The extract was made in *tris* buffer at pH 7·4 containing 10^{-4}M-magnesium. Centrifugation was for 2 h 45 min at 25 000 rev/min. The optical density curve (○) shows the two families of ribosomal particles; the radioactivity curve (●) shows the distribution of the 'pulse-labelled' RNA. (Redrawn from Gros *et al.*[10].)

with the idea that the pulse-labelled RNA was a precursor of the ribosomal RNA; and this interpretation of the kinetics of RNA labelling in *E. coli* had been advanced before the paper by Gros *et al.* appeared[11] and continued to be advanced by some workers after its appearance.[12] However, Gros *et al.* rejected this interpretation because of some additional experiments that they had carried out on *Staphylococcus aureus*. In this organism the pulse-labelled RNA was said to have a base composition resembling that of the DNA, and could not therefore be a precursor of the ribosomal RNA. I shall have occasion somewhat later to discuss in more detail the validity of the techniques used for measuring the base composition of pulse-labelled RNA; but I think it is fair to say that the relationship between the pulse-labelled RNA and ribosomal RNA remains incompletely resolved to the present day. There is, as far as I am aware, no convincing evidence that the base composition of the pulse-labelled RNA resembles that of the DNA, but many studies do suggest that it does have a base composition that differs from that of the ribosomal RNA. Some authors believe, from a detailed study of the distribution of radioactive phosphorus in the nucleotides released by alkali hydrolysis of the pulse-labelled RNA, that about two-thirds of it in bacteria *is* a precursor of ribosomal RNA, and that about one-third of it is something else.[13]

Analysis of the kinetics of turnover of the pulse-labelled RNA in growing bacteria has been, and continues to be, frustrated by two difficulties. The first is that when cells that have been exposed to radioactive RNA precursors are transferred to non-radioactive medium, the RNA precursor pools are only very gradually diluted with non-radioactive material, and radioactivity from these pools continues to enter RNA for some time after the cells have been transferred to the non-radioactive medium.[11] (This is an important point that will come up again when the paper by Brenner *et al.*[9] is considered.) The second is that any acute change in cultural conditions, such as is produced by transferring cells from one medium to another, induces a state of temporary shock in which the normal flow of macromolecular synthesis is disturbed. This state of shock, sometimes called 'step-down', induces a breakdown of RNA that does not occur, or is much less marked, in cells growing in a steady state.[14] Attempts have been made to measure the turnover of pulse-labelled RNA by the use of actinomycin D,[15] which, under some, but not all, conditions,[16] suppresses residual incorporation of radioactivity from the precursor pools when the labelled cells are transferred to non-radioactive medium. But these measurements are still subject to the complication

that actinomycin D induces the degradation of all families of
RNA in the cell,[17] and the pulse-labelled RNA appears to be
especially susceptible to this degradation.[18, 18a] No demonstration
of the physiological instability of the pulse-labelled RNA has
yet been made in bacteria, which would convince the inveterate
doubter; but, if the pulse-labelled RNA does indeed have a base
composition that is different from the other 95 per cent or more
of the RNA in the cell, it would be difficult to avoid the conclusion that at least some of the pulse-labelled RNA must be
involved in rapid turnover.

We have now to consider whether the sedimentation behaviour of the pulse-labelled RNA did in fact reveal the existence of a heterogeneous family of RNA molecules which, at
higher concentrations of magnesium, became attached to the
ribosomes in the cell cytoplasm. A detailed study of this very
question has recently been made by Artman and his colleagues.[19, 20] These authors found that when the pulse-labelled
RNA in *E. coli* was extracted from the cells directly with phenol
at low ionic strength, it did not show the sedimentation
characteristics of the material produced by Gros *et al.*[10] The
sedimentation of the pulse-labelled RNA extracted by phenol
at low ionic strength was indistinguishable from that of the
ribosomal RNA, that is to say, it sedimented as two components having sedimentation coefficients of 23S and 16S. The
behaviour of the pulse-labelled RNA was also indistinguishable
from that of the ribosomal RNA on columns of methylated
albumin. Artman *et al.* found that the pulse-labelled RNA was
very susceptible to mechanical shear, and that the preparative
techniques used by Gros *et al.*, which involved grinding the
bacterial cells with alumina, caused fragmentation of the pulse-
labelled RNA with consequent polydispersity of sedimentation.
When the pulse-labelled RNA was prepared by lysis of bacterial
spheroplasts (cells from which the walls had been removed by
enzymatic digestion), the bulk of it was again found to sediment in the same regions as the ribosomal RNA. A small
amount of radioactivity sedimenting less rapidly than the ribosomal RNA components appeared to be composed of incomplete RNA chains in the process of being synthesized. Sedat,
Lyon, and Sinsheimer[21] have examined the pulse-labelled
RNA in *E. coli* after purification by chromatography on columns

of benzoylated DEAE-cellulose. These authors found that the radioactivity that was not associated with the ribosomal RNA components was relatively homogeneous and had a low average molecular weight (about 72 000). Both Artman *et al.* and Sedat *et al.* agree that the very heterogeneous RNA described by Gros *et al.* and other authors[22-24] is an artefact produced by aggregation of the pulse-labelled RNA with itself and with the ribosomal RNA components. This view is strongly supported by the observation that the polydispersity of the pulse-labelled RNA disappears when it is examined in gradients containing dimethyl sulphoxide[21] which minimizes interactions between and within polynucleotide chains.

Gros *et al.* noted that at higher concentrations of magnesium much of the pulse-labelled RNA sedimented in the position occupied by the 70S ribosomes, and they interpreted this behaviour as evidence that the pulse-labelled RNA became attached to these ribosomes. They noted, however, that this interpretation gave rise to a serious difficulty: 70S ribosomes to which the pulse-labelled RNA was attached should not sediment at 70S, but should be heavier. No satisfactory resolution of this difficulty was provided by Gros *et al.*, but it does appear to have been provided by Artman *et al.*[19] The latter authors showed that the radioactivity sedimenting at 70S at high concentrations of magnesium was not *attached to* ribosomes, but formed an integral part of the 50S and 30S ribosomal subunits, which became associated to form the 70S particle at higher concentrations of magnesium. This view was supported by the failure to release any free RNA from these particles when they were subjected to very low magnesium concentrations. Artman *et al.* conclude that the great bulk of the pulse-labelled RNA in *E. coli* forms an integral part of the newly synthesized ribosomal subunits; and they consider that there is no direct evidence for the existence in normal cells of RNA molecules that are distinct from ribosomal RNA and attach to 70S ribosomes at higher concentrations of magnesium. I do not imagine that the work of Artman *et al.* will prove to be the last word on this subject; but, at the very least, their experiments do make it clear that the effects of magnesium on the sedimentation behaviour of the pulse-labelled RNA are easily susceptible to interpretations other than the one favoured by Gros *et al.*

We come now to the paper by Brenner *et al.*[9] dealing with bacteriophage-infected *E. coli*. It was known at the time that this work was undertaken that when *E. coli* cells were infected with the T-even bacteriophages net synthesis of bacterial RNA was rapidly inhibited.[25] Brenner *et al.* examined the synthesis of RNA in cells infected with phage T4 and reached the following conclusions: (1) that no new ribosomes of any sort were made in the infected bacterial cell; (2) that the RNA made by the phage could be identified by its sedimentation behaviour, which differed from that of the bacterial ribosomal RNA; (3) that the phage messenger RNA was unstable; and (4) that the phage messenger RNA became attached to pre-existing ribosomes and acted as a template for protein synthesis while it was attached to these particles.

The crucial experiment in this paper was the one that purported to demonstrate that no new ribosomes of any sort were made in the infected cell. Clearly, if the phage does not make its own ribosomes and if the phage proteins are made on pre-existing bacterial ribosomes, then the templates produced on the phage DNA must become involved with the bacterial ribosomes in some way. The evidence that no new ribosomes were made in the phage-infected cell was obtained in the following way. The bacteria were grown in heavy isotopes (^{15}N and ^{13}C) until all the cell constituents were uniformly labelled with these isotopes. By means of density gradient centrifugation in caesium chloride it is possible to distinguish the ribosomes extracted from these 'heavy' cells from those extracted from normal 'light' cells, since the 'heavy' ribosomes sediment to a position of higher density in the gradient. The heavy cells were then infected with the phage and transferred to medium containing 'light' isotopes (^{14}N and ^{12}C). After 7 min in this medium the cells were disrupted and the newly formed RNA, labelled from the second to the seventh minute with radioactive phosphorus, was subjected to density gradient centrifugation. The labelled RNA was found to sediment in the position occupied by the 'heavy' ribosomes, not in the position normally occupied by the 'light' ribosomes; from which the conclusion was drawn that no 'wholly new' ribosomes were formed after phage infection. However, a consideration of the behaviour of the RNA precursor pools in *E. coli* indicates that the formation of wholly 'light' ribosomes is hardly to be expected in an experiment of this sort. It is well known that when bacteria are exposed for even a few seconds to a radioactive RNA precursor and then transferred to non-radioactive medium, the radioactive RNA precursor pools are not immediately diluted with unlabelled material, but continue to feed radioactivity into RNA for many minutes afterwards.[11] After exposure for 1 min to radioactive uracil, *E. coli* cells, transferred to non-radioactive medium containing an excess of unlabelled uridine and cytidine, continue to incorporate radioactivity into RNA from the radioactive precursor pools for at least 15 min.[26] We can therefore be confident that if the cells are grown in 'heavy' isotopes until all the RNA precursor pools are uniformly 'heavy', these 'heavy' pools will continue to provide 'heavy' isotopes for RNA synthesis for many minutes after the cells have been transferred to 'light' medium. On the other hand, the amino acid pools are replaced rapidly.[27] One might therefore suppose that at least the newly synthesized ribosomal proteins would be completely 'light'. But there is evidence that the assembly of the ribosome draws on a substantial pool of preformed ribosomal protein,[28-31] so that even the protein moiety of the newly formed ribosomes would remain 'heavy' for some minutes after transfer of the 'heavy' cells to 'light' medium. It will thus be evident that the formation of *completely* 'light' ribosomes is not to be expected within the 7-min period studied by Brenner *et al.*, whether the cells are infected with phage or not. What is to be expected is that the ribosomes synthesized immediately after transfer of the 'heavy' cells to 'light' medium would be essentially 'heavy' and that they would become progressively 'lighter' as the 'heavy' precursor pools became diluted with 'light' material. And, indeed, in the experiments of Brenner *et al.*, although the RNA synthesized after transfer of the 'heavy' cells to 'light' medium sediments with the 'heavy' ribosome band, the sedimentation pattern shows skewing to the 'light' side, which is precisely what our knowledge of the behaviour of the precursor pools predicts that it should do. The experiments of Brenner *et al.* thus do not prove that no new ribosomes are formed after phage infection; indeed, the method can hardly be sensitive enough to provide such a proof. The validity of this criticism has recently been confirmed. It is now clear that *E. coli* cells continue to synthesize many families of bacterial RNA, including ribosomal RNA, for several minutes after infection with phage T4.[32, 33]

Like Gros *et al.*, Brenner *et al.* concluded that the RNA made by the phage became attached to bacterial ribosomes at high concentrations of magnesium. The objections to this conclusion and the relevance of the recent study of Artman *et al.* on this point have already been discussed.[19] The finding that at high magnesium concentrations the newly formed RNA sediments in the *same* position as the bacterial ribosomes argues *against* the idea that this RNA is *attached to* these ribosomes. If it were, the RNA-ribosomes complex would have a higher ratio of RNA to protein than the ribosomes alone and would therefore sediment to a position of higher density in the caesium chloride gradient. The fact that the newly formed RNA sediments in the same position as the ribosomes suggests that it is an integral part of the ribosome or of some other particle having the same density. Finally, Brenner *et al.* concluded that much of the labelled phage RNA underwent intracellular degradation. There can be little objection to this conclusion, since their experiments showed a net loss of radioactivity from the RNA of the infected cell. But the biological significance of this RNA degradation is far from clear. Cells infected with the T-even phages are in a state of acute 'step-down', which is known to induce an abnormal degradation of RNA; and we do not know whether the RNA molecules that are being degraded are the ones that specify the synthesis of the phage proteins.

3. The rapidly labelled RNA in the cell nucleus

The most detailed studies on RNA metabolism that have so far been made have been carried out on animal cells, and especially on animal cells cultivated *in vitro*. I therefore propose to deal mainly with this material, but I shall draw from time to time on data derived from experiments with bacteria. Once again, the bacterial and animal cell systems appear to me to be very similar.

When animal cells are exposed for 10 to 15 min to a radioactive RNA precursor, more than 90 per cent of the radioactivity is found to be located in the cell nucleus. The fact that radioactive precursors first label the RNA in the cell nucleus was discovered by Bergstrand *et al.*[34] in 1948; and the relationship between the initial nuclear labelling and the subsequent cytoplasmic labelling has since been the subject of an extensive and complex literature.[35] The situation seems to be quite the same in bacteria. When bacteria that have a moderately well-defined nuclear area, such as *E. coli*, are exposed for about a minute to a radioactive RNA precursor, most of the radioactivity is localized in the bacterial 'nucleus';[36] and more prolonged exposure to the radioactive precursor labels the bacterial cytoplasm. In animal cells this rapidly labelled nuclear RNA is not free in solution, but still appears to be attached in some way to the chromosomes.[37-39] The mode of attachment has not yet been clarified: it may be that the newly formed RNA is still bound to its DNA template by hydrogen bonds between the DNA and RNA strands, but there is some evidence that protein may be involved.[40] Whether the rapidly labelled RNA in bacteria is also attached to the bacterial chromosome is not known. In order to study this RNA in bacteria it is usually necessary to disrupt the cells and then treat the disrupted preparation with deoxyribonuclease in order to reduce its viscosity. Such treatment, of course, destroys the bacterial chromosome and thus vitiates any assessment of what might or might not be attached to it *in vivo*.

When rapidly labelled RNA is extracted from the nuclei of animal cells it shows some unusual physical properties. In sucrose density gradients its sedimentation behaviour has proved to be extraordinarily variable. The following sedimentation patterns have been described, among others: heterogeneous material sedimenting in the same areas as the 28S and 16S components;†[37] heterogeneous material sedimenting partly with the 28S and 16S components and partly less rapidly;[41] heterogeneous material sedimenting partly with the 28S and 16S components and partly more rapidly;[42-46] two broad but relatively homogeneous components separating at 45S and 35S;[47] extremely polydisperse material having a continuous range of sedimentation coefficients from about 80S to 10S.[48] A commonly observed pattern is shown in Fig. 5. This state of affairs is not very different from that found in bacteria. Although the original papers of Brenner *et al.*[9] and Gros *et al.*[10] showed the rapidly labelled RNA in *E. coli* as a broad peak with

†See additional note on page 79.

a sedimentation coefficient somewhere between 8S and 16S, much more heterogeneous sedimentation behaviour has since been described.[22-24] The evidence in support of the view that much of this heterogeneity is due to aggregation of the rapidly labelled RNA has already been discussed.[19-21]

The sedimentation behaviour of the rapidly labelled RNA in

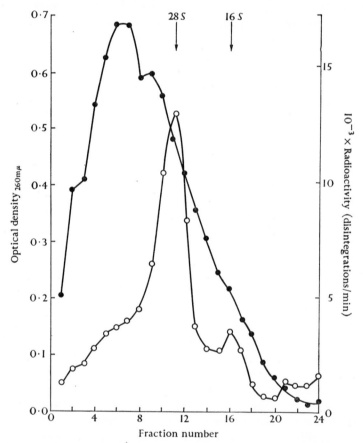

FIG. 5 Sucrose-density-gradient sedimentation pattern of nuclear RNA extracted from HeLa cells after a 15 min exposure to [³H]uridine. The RNA was extracted by the use of phenol and detergent and was treated with 2M-sodium chloride to remove DNA degradation products. The gradient contained 50 mM-sodium chloride and 10 mM-EDTA at pH 7·4. Centrifugation was for 3·5 h at 37 500 rev/min. The optical density curve (○) shows the 28S and 16S RNA components; the radioactivity curve (●) shows the distribution of the 'pulse-labelled' RNA. (From Bramwell and Harris.[49])

animal cells has recently been subjected to a detailed examination which also suggests that the gross polydispersity is essentially an experimental artefact.[49] Due to the fact that this RNA
has very little secondary structure, its shape and the extent to
which it aggregates with itself and with other macromolecules
is greatly influenced by the method of preparation and by the
ionic strength and cation concentration of the medium in which
it is examined. Almost any sedimentation coefficient can be
obtained by appropriate manipulation of physical conditions.
However, when highly purified preparations of the rapidly
labelled RNA are examined at low ionic strength and after
removal of divalent cations, their sedimentation in sucrose
gradients is very similar to that of the 16S component of the
ribosomal RNA (Fig. 6). Sedimentation of the rapidly labelled
RNA in gradients of sulpholane, which reduces interactions
between RNA molecules, also eliminates the polydispersity and,
under certain conditions, resolves the rapidly labelled material
in the region of the smaller ribosomal RNA component.[50]
These findings resemble the observations made by Artman
et al.[19, 20] in E. coli where the rapidly labelled RNA extracted
from the cell by phenol at low ionic strength was found to have
a sedimentation indistinguishable from that of the bacterial
ribosomal RNA. But similarity of sedimentation pattern in a
sucrose density gradient does not necessarily mean similarity
of molecular weight; and two other methods have therefore
been used to measure the chain length of the polynucleotides in
the rapidly labelled RNA. In one, this was measured by a
technique that involved digestion of the rapidly labelled RNA
under controlled conditions with a purified exonuclease;[51] in
the other alkali hydrolysis was used to determine the proportion
of the total nucleotides released as end groups.[52] By both
methods the mean polynucleotide chain length of the rapidly
labelled RNA was found to be very close to that of the ribosomal RNA. This conclusion has been questioned by Granboulan
and Scherrer[53] who have made electron microscopic measurements of RNA fractions separated by centrifugation. These
authors consider that the polydisperse material that sediments
more rapidly than the ribosomal RNA does consist of single
polynucleotide chains. It may, however, be doubted whether
electron microscopy of coated preparations would distinguish

between single polynucleotide chains and strands of RNA composed of two or more overlapping chains. Indeed, the data presented by Granboulan and Scherrer strongly suggest that their preparations do contain aggregates of some sort, for the measurements given for the relatively homogeneous ribosomal RNA components show a very wide distribution of chain lengths including some up to three times the size corresponding to the known molecular weight of the ribosomal RNA

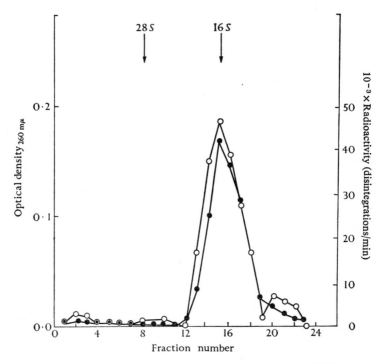

FIG. 6. Sucrose-density-gradient sedimentation pattern of nuclear RNA extracted from HeLa cells after a 15 min exposure to [³H]uridine. The RNA was prepared in the same way as the sample shown in Fig. 5, but was treated for 45 min at 21° with 5 mM-EDTA in water to remove magnesium. The gradient contained 5 mM-EDTA-*tris* buffer at pH 7·0. Centrifugation was for 5 h at 37 500 rev/min. The optical density curve (○) shows that, after removal of magnesium, all the nuclear RNA sediments as a single component with a sedimentation coefficient of about 16S; and the radioactivity curve(●) shows that the 'pulse-labelled' RNA also sediments as a single 16S component under these conditions. This effect is reversible. A pattern similar to that shown in Fig. 5 can be produced again when the ionic strength and magnesium concentration are increased. (From Bramwell and Harris.[49])

components. It therefore seems unlikely that these electron microscopic measurements provide a reliable estimate of polynucleotide chain length.

Is it possible, then, that the rapidly labelled RNA is simply a precursor of the ribosomal RNA, as was originally thought to be the case? Its unusual sedimentation behaviour does not decisively distinguish it from ribosomal RNA. One might expect that the newly made RNA, which is extracted while it is still attached to the chromosome, would show a poorly ordered structure; and the more stable structure characteristic of ribosomal RNA could easily be imposed on the rapidly labelled RNA by methylation of the sugar,[54, 55] by secondary modification of certain bases, by the attachment of protein, or by all three. Two lines of evidence bear on this question. The first involves kinetic analysis of the passage of radioactivity through the RNA of the cell; the second, measurement of the base composition of the rapidly labelled RNA. Shortly after the discovery that the RNA in the cell nucleus was the first to become labelled by radioactive RNA precursors,[34] it was shown that when briefly labelled cells were transferred to non-radioactive medium, radioactivity left the nuclear RNA and appeared in the cytoplasmic RNA. This experiment, carried out by both chemical and autoradiographic methods, was confirmed in many different cells, and was generally interpreted to mean that the rapidly labelled RNA in the cell nucleus was the precursor of the more slowly labelled RNA in the cytoplasm.[56] When the sedimentation characteristics of ribosomal RNA were established, similar experiments showed that the disappearance of the radioactivity from the rapidly labelled RNA was associated with the appearance of radioactivity in the ribosomal RNA;[11] and it was therefore commonly believed that the rapidly labelled RNA was the precursor of the ribosomal RNA.

This idea was first questioned in 1959, when it was observed that there were major discrepancies between the amount of radioactivity lost from the nuclear RNA and the amount that appeared in the cytoplasmic RNA.[57, 58] An extensive series of experiments eventually established that much of the rapidly labelled nuclear RNA was involved in a process of intracellular turnover: this RNA was not only rapidly made, but also rapidly broken down in the cell.[37, 59, 60] This conclusion, which had, in fact, been reached 2 years before the 'messenger' hypothesis was launched, and thus came 2 years too soon,[57, 58] was initially received with little enthusiasm; but it has now been confirmed in a wide range of different cells[46, 48, 61-65] and appears to be generally accepted. In cells growing exponentially, ribosomal RNA appears to be essentially stable,[4] and in non-growing cells, it turns over at a very much slower rate than the rapidly labelled RNA.[66] We can therefore conclude, whether the rapidly labelled RNA is a macromolecular precursor of ribosomal RNA or not, that the bulk of it is not in fact converted into ribosomal RNA under the usual experimental conditions.

Measurement of the base composition of the rapidly labelled RNA has been fraught with great difficulty. Until very recently it has not been possible to isolate this material and determine its base composition by direct chemical analysis. An indirect method introduced by Volkin and Astrachan[67] in 1956 has been extensively used; the cells are exposed for a short period of time to radioactive phosphate and the distribution of radio-activity in the nucleotides obtained by alkali hydrolysis of the labelled RNA is taken as a measure of the base composition of the rapidly labelled fraction. This technique can obviously only be a measure of base composition if certain assumptions are made about the randomness of the distribution of the radio-active phosphorus in the polynucleotide chains. I think it is enough to say that, after extensive investigation, it is now clear that these assumptions do not hold when the cells are exposed to a radioactive RNA precursor for short periods of time, and that, consequently, the 'phosphorus pulse' method, as this technique is called, does not provide a reliable estimate of the base composition of the rapidly labelled RNA.[68-70] The extreme variability of the results obtained with this technique, the discovery of RNA fractions having a base composition resembling that of the DNA, the equally frequent failure to detect such DNA-like fractions, the dramatic changes in the composition of the rapidly labelled RNA produced by external stimuli or by changes in cultural conditions, are all reflections of the fact that the distribution of radioactivity in RNA after a short pulse of radioactive phosphorus is influenced by factors other than the base composition of the RNA synthesized during the pulse.

The unusual physical characteristics of the rapidly labelled RNA have, however, provided a method for its isolation, and hence for the direct determination of its base composition. Perhaps because it has so little secondary structure, the rapidly labelled RNA adheres tightly to columns of methylated albumin on kieselguhr at salt concentrations that elute all the other ribonucleic acids in the cell.[71] The RNA that adheres to methylated albumin is normally present in the cell only in trace amounts, but it has recently been found that this RNA accumulates within the cell nucleus when cells are subjected to acute 'step-down'.[72] Easily measurable amounts of rapidly labelled, polydisperse RNA can be isolated from cells treated in this way and its base composition can then be determined by direct measurement of the amounts of the four RNA nucleotides released by alkaline hydrolysis. Measured in this way, the base composition of the rapidly labelled RNA proves to be indistinguishable from that of the 16S RNA extracted from the smaller ribosomal sub-unit.[72] This finding lends strong support to the view that the rapidly labelled RNA is, in large part, an early form of at least one of the ribosomal RNA components, a view further reinforced by the observation that the distribution of methylated ribose residues among the base sequences of the rapidly labelled RNA is indistinguishable from that found in the ribosomal RNA.[73] If the rapidly labelled RNA is indeed an early stage in the formation of 16S ribosomal RNA, its rapid turnover must reflect the fact that only a small part of the precursor is converted into mature ribosomal RNA under the usual experimental conditions. I shall have more to say about this at a later stage.

4. '45S' RNA

Under certain conditions of extraction and centrifugation, some of the rapidly labelled RNA may sediment as a rather broad peak of radioactivity in a region of the sucrose gradient that corresponds to a sedimentation coefficient of about 45S.[47] When cells that have been briefly exposed to a radioactive RNA precursor are transferred to non-radioactive medium, radioactivity leaves the 45S region and appears in the 28S and 16S ribosomal RNA peaks; and this process continues to a small extent in the presence of moderate concentrations of

actinomycin D.[74] The conclusion has therefore been drawn
that the 45S RNA is the precursor of both the 28S and the 16S
ribosomal RNA. On the assumption that 45S RNA is a single
covalently linked polynucleotide chain, it has been proposed
that 28S and 16S ribosomal RNA are generated by asym-
metrical splitting of this single giant macromolecular precursor;[75] but since this precursor (assuming a simple relationship
between chain length and sedimentation coefficient) would be
about twice the length of a molecule composed of one 28S and
one 16S sub-unit, it has been further postulated that about
half of the molecule undergoes degradation when the 28S
and 16S components are split off.[76, 77]

This is, on the face of it, an intrinsically improbable scheme,
and strong evidence would be required to ensure its acceptance.
Recent studies, in fact, make it very difficult to accept. To begin with, if the 28S and 16S RNA components were formed by
scission of a single larger precursor, one might expect that
when cells are exposed to a radioactive RNA precursor, radioactivity would always enter 28S and 16S RNA at the same rate.
It is, however, a common experience that radioactivity appears
in 16S nuclear RNA before it appears in 28S nuclear RNA; and
the labelling of these two components can easily be further dis-
sociated by a variety of experimental procedures.[78-80] Two
groups of workers have examined the distribution of radioactivity in oligonucleotides released by partial digestion of
28S and 16S RNA from cells exposed for a short period to a
radioactive RNA precursor. Both find that the labelling patterns of 28S RNA and 16S RNA are very different, a finding
difficult to reconcile with the idea that these components arise
by the scission of a single polynucleotide chain.[81-83] And Bramwell has shown that RNA indistinguishable from 16S RNA,
both in base composition and in sedimentation behaviour under
appropriate conditions, can accumulate in the cell nucleus
when the synthesis of 28S RNA has been completely suppressed
by low doses of actinomycin D.[72] All these findings make it
very improbable that 28S and 16S RNA are split off from a
single larger precursor, a scheme that would hardly have been
proposed in the first instance were it not for the assumption that
polydisperse RNA components that sediment more rapidly
than the ribosomal RNA represent single covalently linked

polynucleotides of enormous length. The arguments against this assumption have already been discussed.

5. Rapidly labelled RNA in the cell cytoplasm

If some of the rapidly labelled nuclear RNA consists of 'messengers' that carry information from the genes to the cytoplasm of the cell, it should be possible to detect such molecules in the cytoplasm. An exhaustive search carried out in many laboratories, with a variety of techniques, and extending over a period of many years, has, however, failed to detect in the cytoplasm of animal cells any RNA fraction that resembles the rapidly labelled RNA in the cell nucleus.[37,42,46,48,49,64,84-88] The first indication that the cytoplasm might not contain any RNA like the rapidly labelled nuclear RNA came with the observation that, under the usual conditions of sucrose gradient centrifugation, preparations of the total RNA in the cell cytoplasm, extracted by direct treatment with phenol and detergent, did not show any fraction that had either the kinetic characteristics or the polydisperse sedimentation of the rapidly labelled nuclear RNA.[37,42] When it became clear that the variable polydispersity of the rapidly labelled RNA was a reflection of its sensitivity to changes in ionic strength and cation concentration, the RNA in the cytoplasm was examined in solutions of varying ionic strength and cation concentration, but still no RNA showing the physical characteristics of the rapidly labelled nuclear RNA was revealed.[49] Finally, the ability of columns of methylated albumin to select the rapidly labelled RNA from a heterogeneous mixture of other ribonucleic acids permitted the cytoplasmic RNA to be screened by this technique also. But again, no RNA having the properties of the rapidly labelled nuclear RNA could be found.[88]

I am not aware that any one at present disputes the conclusion that no RNA having the physical or kinetic characteristics of the rapidly labelled nuclear RNA is to be found in the cytoplasm of the cell. This RNA can be detected only in the cell nucleus, and the rapid turnover that it undergoes appears to be effected by intranuclear degradation. This conclusion, like the discovery of the turnover itself, was also received with little enthusiasm when it was first reported;[37] but numerous studies involving measurement of the kinetics of RNA labelling, sedimentation analysis, and examination of the nature and distribution of the degradative enzymes now support the view that much of the rapidly labelled nuclear RNA undergoes degradation within the nucleus.[37,46,48,63,64,89-98] The functional significance of intranuclear RNA turnover has not yet been resolved, but some plausible suggestions have been made. The short-lived nuclear RNA may be implicated in the synthesis of some nuclear proteins,[100] although why the templates for these nuclear proteins should be much less stable than the templates for cytoplasmic proteins is obscure. It may be engaged in the regulation of genetic activity,[101] although no precise mechanism for the RNA-mediated regulation has yet been put forward. Or it may simply be a reflection of the fact that only a small proportion of the RNA that is transcribed from the DNA passes to the cytoplasm to function as a template. I personally favour the last alternative, and I shall present evidence in a later chapter in support of the view that the limiting step in the transfer of information from the genes to the cytoplasm is not the synthesis of the template but its incorporation into a structure that resists intranuclear degradation. I shall argue that the RNA made on the genes must be 'engaged' by the mechanisms that confer resistance to intranuclear degradation before this RNA can be transported to the cytoplasm. On this view, the RNA that is broken down within the nucleus is the material that fails to be 'engaged' by these mechanisms.

While it now appears to be generally agreed that the cytoplasm does not contain any RNA having the characteristics of the rapidly labelled nuclear RNA, other minor RNA components have from time to time been described in the cytoplasm and have been canvassed as the 'messenger' molecules postulated by Jacob and Monod. When RNA is extracted directly from the cell cytoplasm with phenol and detergent, no RNA components of high molecular weight are detected, either by ultraviolet absorption or by their radioactive content, apart from the ribosomal RNA.[37,49,86] But when radioactive cells are disrupted by homogenization, and preparations of cytoplasmic ribosomes are made, minor labelled components are sometimes revealed that sediment apart from the ribosomes. It is now clear that the great majority of these minor components, whether they are found as free RNA or as RNA-protein complexes, are artefacts arising from nuclear damage produced during cell fractionation. When cells are exposed for a short period to a radioactive RNA precursor, the specific activity of the RNA in the cell nucleus may be two or three orders of magnitude higher than that of the RNA in the cytoplasm. Under such conditions the rupture of a few nuclei per thousand cells may release traces of radioactive RNA or radioactive ribonucleoprotein into what is eventually collected as the 'cytoplasmic' fraction. Probably no fractionation procedure currently available is completely free from this source of error. Indeed, it has been shown that when pulse-labelled cells are fractionated by standard homogenization procedures, the amount of pulse-labelled RNA appearing in the 'cytoplasmic' fraction increases as homogenization proceeds.[102]

If, as has been postulated, the rapidly labelled RNA in the cell cytoplasm is attached to ribosomes, it should be possible to find ribosomal particles in the cytoplasm carrying this additional RNA. Perry and Kelley[103] have searched for such complexes by examining the buoyant density of formaldehyde-fixed ribosomal particles in caesium chloride density gradients. Ribosomal particles with additional RNA attached to them would have a higher ratio of RNA to protein than particles without additional RNA and would therefore be expected to sediment to a position of higher density in the gradient. Perry and Kelley were unable to detect in the cytoplasm of normal cells any particles having a higher density than the ribosomal subunits themselves; and they therefore concluded that the cytoplasm did not contain any ribosomal particles with additional RNA attached to them. However, Perry and Kelley did find some particles that sedimented in regions of lower density than the ribosomal subunits. These particles, which showed some heterogeneity in their sedimentation behaviour, became radioactive more rapidly than the ribosomal subunits when the cells were exposed to a radioactive RNA precursor. The fact that these particles were less dense than ribosomal subunits was thought to indicate either that they had a lower ratio of RNA to protein or that they were more highly hydrated. Such particles have been found in several different kinds of cells[104–107] and, in the hope that they might be specifically involved in the transfer of genetic information from nucleus to cytoplasm, they have been called 'informosomes'. There is as yet no evidence that these particles do serve this function, and, indeed, it is not clear whether they are normally present in the cell or whether they are complexes formed by interaction between RNA and protein during cell fractionation. A more recent investigation by Perry and Kelley[108] suggests that the great bulk of these particles may be derived from damaged nuclei.

Examination of the cytoplasmic contents of disrupted reticulocytes has revealed the presence of a minor RNA component that sediments in the 9S region;[69,109] and evidence has been presented in support of the view that this minor component is the messenger RNA for haemoglobin.[110-112] This evidence is not yet conclusive; but even if the templates for haemoglobin were found to sediment in this region, this finding would not greatly further the search for a means of identifying messenger RNA as a class. What is required is a general method that would permit the identification of messenger RNA in the cell cytoplasm by virtue of some chemical or physical features peculiar to this class of molecules. Rapidity of labelling and polydispersity of sedimentation have not so far proved useful in making such an identification.

6. 'Polysomes'

It has been known for many years that the ribosomes in the cell cytoplasm are sometimes associated together in clusters of various sizes, and sometimes in groups with more elaborate configurations. With the advent of the 'messenger' hypothesis the idea was put forward that these clusters were held together by a strand of 'messenger' RNA and were thus the principal sites of protein synthesis in the cell.[113-115] The idea that these clusters, which were renamed 'polysomes', were held together by a strand of 'messenger' RNA rested mainly on the finding that they fell apart when treated with very low concentrations of ribonuclease.[115,116] Some electron micrographs of isolated 'polysomes' also appeared to show the ribosomes connected by some form of strand.[116] In view of the failure of biochemical methods to detect this strand in the cytoplasm of the cell, the question arises whether the 'polysomes' are in fact joined together by an RNA strand. The sensitivity of these structures to ribonuclease is an inconclusive argument: the ribosomal RNA

at the surface of the ribosomes may itself be involved in main-
taining the structure of the aggregate, and even very low concentrations of ribonuclease may break essential bonds at the
periphery of the ribosomal RNA without grossly disrupting the
ribosome as a whole. This is not merely a theoretical possibility.
A recent study of this problem has shown that any concentration
of ribonuclease that will disaggregate 'polysomes' also produces
some degradation of the ribosomal RNA.[117] If the ribosomes
were indeed held together by a strand of RNA, one would
expect this strand to be more susceptible to attack by
ribonuclease than the RNA in the ribosomes; and it should be
possible to find concentrations of ribonuclease that would disaggregate 'polysomes' without degrading the ribosomal RNA.
The fact that this cannot be achieved argues against the
presence of a strand of RNA that is more susceptible to degradation than the ribosomal RNA itself. Electron microscopic
observations on 'polysomes' isolated from *E. coli* suggest that
the ribosomes are held together by contacts between their
subunits,[118] so that disaggregation could easily be produced by
nuclease attack at sensitive sites in the ribosomal RNA;[117] and
the demonstration that heterogeneous RNA of variable sedimentation may be released by procedures that disaggregate
'polysomes' must be open to the suspicion that the heterogeneous RNA is generated by degradation of ribosomal RNA.
In some cases, the 'polysomes' are relatively resistant to ribonucleases, but are readily disaggregated by proteases.[119-123]
Indeed, more detailed studies on the fine structure of ribosomal
aggregates suggest that their structure is too complicated to be
maintained simply by a strand of RNA, and there is some
evidence in both bacterial and animal cells that the 'polysomes' are held together by a complex fibrillary network that
may consist of protein.[124-126] And even in cases where a more
complex structure appears to be unlikely, the possibility that
the ribosomes are held together by nascent polypeptide chains
or by other proteins cannot easily be eliminated. There is
good evidence, from studies with intact cells as well as disrupted cell preparations, that the formation and maintenance
of liver 'polysomes' depends upon the availability of amino
acids;[127-129] and reticulocyte 'polysomes', disaggregated *in vitro*,
can be induced to reaggregate and resume protein synthesis

when a soluble protein present in the supernatant fraction of reticulocyte cytoplasm is added to the preparation.[130] There is also some evidence that suggests that the structure of 'polysomes' in *E. coli* may be maintained by the peptidyl-transfer RNA complexes.[131] It is clear that the detailed structure of 'polysomes' is not yet settled. The data available give the impression that ribosomes are often assembled into clusters or more elaborate structures when protein synthesis takes place; but such structures do not appear to be essential for protein synthesis,[132] and there is no decisive evidence that the ribosomes are held together by a strand of 'messenger' RNA.

6. Synthesis of artificial polypeptides in cell-free systems

The results obtained with disrupted cell systems constitute the most formidable support for the 'messenger' RNA hypothesis. It is abundantly clear that synthetic polynucleotides added to preparations of ribosomes do function as templates for the synthesis of polypeptides;[133] and it would be gratuitous to point out how much we have learnt about the nature of the genetic code from experiments involving the use of these synthetic messengers.[134] However, I do not believe that the success of this system inevitably implies that the synthesis of protein in the cytoplasm of the intact cell is also programmed by templates that attach to ribosomes in the same way. In this system, the artificial polynucleotide is added to the ribosomes in great excess, and only a small proportion of the amount added forms a stable attachment to the ribosomes and functions as a template.[135] It could be argued that the added polynucleotide is superimposed on the normal template surface of the ribosome and that the synthesis of the polypeptide takes place on the added polynucleotide because the normal template is masked. The intracellular behaviour of RNA-containing bacteriophages lends support to this idea. A recent study of *E. coli* cells infected with these bacteriophages has shown that the phage RNA does become attached to the ribosomes of the cell to form complexes that can be identified by their increased density in caesium chloride gradients and their increased sedimentation velocity in sucrose gradients.[136] When the RNA of these bacteriophages is used to program the synthesis of specific phage proteins in disrupted cell systems, it is probable that similar RNA-ribosome complexes are formed.[137-139] But such complexes can not be detected in the uninfected cell. This suggests that the RNA templates produced by the cell itself do not normally form complexes like those formed by the bacteriophage RNA. There is every reason to suppose that artificial polynucleotides in disrupted cell systems become attached to ribosomes in much the same way as bacteriophage RNA; but the available evidence does not support the view that normal cellular templates are introduced into the ribosomal system in this way. By this I do not wish to imply that there are fundamental differences in the mechanism of protein synthesis between infected and uninfected cells; but I do think it likely that there are very real differences in the mechanisms by which the templates become integrated into the ribosomal system. This idea will be discussed in more detail later.

REFERENCES

1. JACOB, F. and MONOD, J. (1961). Genetic regulatory mechanisms in the synthesis of proteins. *J. molec. Biol.* **3**, 318.
2. HERSHEY, A. D. (1954). Conservation of nucleic acids during bacterial growth. *J. gen. Physiol.* **38**, 145.
3. LABAW, L. W., MOSLEY, V. M., and WYCKOFF, R. W. G. (1950). Radioactive studies of the phosphorus metabolism of *Escherichia coli*. *J. Bact.* **59**, 251.
4. SIMINOVITCH, L. S. and GRAHAM, A. F. (1956). Significance of ribonucleic acid and deoxyribonucleic acid turnover studies. *J. Histochem. Cytochem.* **4**, 508.
5. DAVERN, C. I. and MESELSON, M. (1960). The molecular conservation of ribonucleic acid during bacterial growth. *J. molec. Biol.* **2**, 153.
6. BELOZERSKY, A. N. and SPIRIN, A. S. (1958). A correlation between the compositions of deoxyribonucleic acid and ribonucleic acid. *Nature, Lond.* **182**, 111.
7. CHARGAFF, E. (1955). Isolation and composition of the deoxypentose nucleic acids and of the corresponding nucleoproteins. *The nucleic acids* (Eds. E. CHARGAFF and J. N. DAVIDSON), p. 307. Academic Press, New York.
8. MAGASANIK, B. (1955). Isolation and composition of the pentose nucleic acids and of the corresponding nucleoproteins. *The nucleic acids* (Eds. E. CHARGAFF and J. N. DAVIDSON), p. 373. Academic Press, New York.
9. BRENNER, S., JACOB, F., and MESELSON, M. (1961). An unstable intermediate carrying information from genes to ribosomes for protein synthesis. *Nature, Lond.* **190**, 576.

10. Gros, F., Hiatt, H., Gilbert, W., Kurland, C. G., Risebrough, R. W., and Watson, J. D. (1961). Unstable ribonucleic acid revealed by pulse labelling of *Escherichia coli*. *Nature, Lond.* **190,** 581.

11. Aronson, A. I., Bolton, E. T., Britten, R. J., Cowie, D. B., Duerksen, J. D., McCarthy, B. J., McQuillen, K., and Roberts, R. B. (1960). *Carnegie Institution of Washington Year Book* **59,** 229.

12. Kitazume, Y., Yčas, M., and Vincent, W. S. (1962). Metabolic properties of a ribonucleic acid fraction in yeast. *Proc. natn. Acad. Sci. U.S.A.* **48,** 265.

13. Midgley, J. E. M. and McCarthy, B. J. (1962). The synthesis and kinetic behaviour of deoxyribonucleic acid-like ribonucleic acid in bacteria. *Biochim. biophys. Acta* **61,** 696.

14. Bellamy, A. R. (1966). RNA synthesis in exponentially growing tobacco cells subjected to a step-down nutritional shift. *Biochim. biophys. Acta* **123,** 102.

15. Levinthal, C., Keynan, A., and Higa, A. (1962). Messenger RNA turnover and protein synthesis in *B. subtilis* inhibited by actinomycin D. *Proc. natn. Acad. Sci. U.S.A.* **48,** 1631.

16. Harris, H. (1964). Breakdown of nuclear ribonucleic acid in the presence of actinomycin D. *Nature, Lond.* **202,** 1301.

17. Wiesner, R., Acs, G., Reich, E., and Shafiq, A. (1965). Degradation of ribonucleic acid in mouse fibroblasts treated with actinomycin. *J. Cell Biol.* **27,** 47.

18. Acs, G., Reich, E., and Valanju, S. (1963). RNA metabolism in *B. subtilis. Biochim. biophys. Acta* **76,** 68.

18a.Stewart, G. H. and Farber, E. (1968). The rapid acceleration of hepatic nuclear ribonucleic acid breakdown by actinomycin but not by ethionine. *J. biol. Chem.* **243,** 4479.

19. Artman, M., Silman, N., and Engelberg, H. (1967). Pulse labelled RNA associated with ribosomes in *Escherichia coli. Nature, Lond.* **213,** 39.

20. Fry, M. and Artman, M. (1968). Sedimentation behaviour of rapidly labelled RNA from *Escherichia coli. Nature, Lond.* **217,** 661.

21. Sedat, J., Lyon, A., and Sinsheimer, R. L. (1969). Purification of *Escherichia coli* pulse-labelled RNA by benzoylated DEAE-cellulose chromatography. *J. molec. Biol.* **44,** 415.

22. Monier, R., Naono, S., Hayes, D., Hayes, F., and Gros, F. (1962). Studies on the heterogeneity of messenger RNA from *E. coli. J. molec. Biol.* **5,** 311.

23. Ishihama, A., Mizuno, N., Takai, M., Otaka, E., and Osawa, S. (1962). Molecular and metabolic properties of messenger RNA from normal and T2-infected *Escherichia coli. J. molec. Biol.* **5,** 251.

24. Asano, K. (1965). Size heterogeneity of T2 messenger RNA. *J. molec. Biol.* **14,** 71.

25. Cohen, S. S. (1949). Growth requirements of bacterial viruses. *Bact. Rev.* **13,** 1.

26. Harris, H. Unpublished data.

27. Britten, R. J. and McClure, F. T. (1962). The amino acid pool in *Escherichia coli. Bact. Rev.* **26,** 292.

28. DALGARNO, L. and GROS, F. (1968). Completion of ribosomal particles in *Escherichia coli* during inhibition of protein synthesis. *Biochim. biophys. Acta* **157**, 52.

29. SANTER, M., RUEBUSH, T. K., BRUNT, J. V., OLDMIXON, E., HESS, R., PRIMAKOFF, P., and PALADE, P. (1968). Identification of a precursor pool of ribosome protein in *Escherichia coli*. *J. Bact.* **95**, 1355.

30. GIERER, L. and GIERER, A. (1968). Synthesis of ribosomal protein and formation of ribosomes in *Escherichia coli*. *J. molec. Biol.* **34**, 293.

31. MARCHIS–MOUREN, G., COZZONE, A., and MARVALDI, J. (1969). Ribosomal protein pools in *Escherichia coli*. *Biochim. biophys. Acta* **N31**, 232.

32. LANDY, A. and SPIEGELMAN, S. (1968). Exhaustive hybridization and its application to an analysis of the ribonucleic acid synthesized in T4-infected cells. *Biochemistry, N.Y.* **7**, 585.

33. KENNELL, D. (1968). Inhibition of host protein synthesis during infection of *Escherichia coli* by bacteriophage T4. I. Continued synthesis of host ribonucleic acid. *J. Virol.* **2**, 1262.

34. BERGSTRAND, A., ELIASSON, N. A., HAMMARSTEN, E., NORBERG, B., REICHARD, P., and VON UBISCH, H. (1948). Experiments with ^{15}N on purines from nuclei and cytoplasm of normal and regenerating liver. *Cold Spring Harb. Symp. quant. Biol.* **13**, 22.

35. HARRIS, H. (1963). Nuclear ribonucleic acid. *Prog. nucl. Acid. Res.* **2**, 20. Academic Press, New York.

36. CARO, L. G. and FORRO, F. (1961). Localization of macromolecules in *Escherichia coli*. *J. biophys. biochem. Cytol.* **9**, 555.

37. HARRIS, H., FISHER, H. W., RODGERS, A., SPENCER, T., and WATTS, J. W. (1963). An examination of the ribonucleic acids in the HeLa cell with special reference to current theory about the transfer of information from nucleus to cytoplasm. *Proc. R. Soc.* B **157**, 177.

38. CRAWLEY, J. C. W. and HARRIS, H. (1963). The fine structure of isolated HeLa cell nuclei. *Expl Cell Res.* **31**, 70.

39. LACOUR, L. F. (1964). Behaviour of nucleoli in isolated nuclei. *Expl Cell Res.* **34**, 239.

40. BONNER, J., HUANG, R.-C., and MAHESHWARI, N. (1961). The physical state of newly synthesized RNA. *Proc. natn. Acad. Sci. U.S.A.* **47**, 1548.

41. CHENG, P.-Y. (1961). Size of rapidly labelled ribonucleic acids in human amnion cells. *Biochim. biophys. Acta* **53**, 235.

42. HIATT, H. H. (1962). A rapidly labeled RNA in rat liver nuclei. *J. molec. Biol.* **5**, 217.

43. PERRY, R. P. (1962). The cellular sites of synthesis of ribosomal and 4*S* RNA. *Proc. natn. Acad. Sci. U.S.A.* **48**, 2179.

44. KIDSON, C., KIRBY, K. S., and RALPH, R. K. (1963). Isolation characteristics of rapidly labeled RNA from normal rat liver. *J. molec. Biol.* **7**, 312.

45. FENWICK, M. L. (1964). The fate of rapidly labelled ribonucleic acid in the presence of actinomycin in normal and virus-infected animal cells. *Biochim. biophys. Acta* **87**, 388.

46. ROBERTS, W. K. (1965). Studies on RNA synthesis in Ehrlich ascites

cells. Extraction and properties of labelled RNA. *Biochim. biophys. Acta* **108**, 474.

47. SCHERRER, K. and DARNELL, J. E. (1962). Sedimentation characteristics of rapidly labelled RNA from HeLa cells. *Biochem. biophys. Res. Commun.* **7**, 486.

48. ATTARDI, G., PARNAS, H., HWANG, M., and ATTARDI, B. (1966). Giant-size rapidly labeled nuclear RNA and cytoplasmic messenger RNA in immature duck erythrocytes. *J. molec. Biol.* **20**, 145.

49. BRAMWELL, M. E. and HARRIS, H. (1967). The origin of the polydispersity in sedimentation patterns of rapidly labelled nuclear RNA. *Biochem. J.* **103**, 816.

50. PARISH, J. H. and KIRBY, K. S. (1966). Reagents which reduce interactions between ribosomal RNA and rapidly labelled RNA from rat liver. *Biochim. biophys. Acta* **129**, 554.

51. RILEY, W. T. (1969). Polynucleotide chain lengths of rapidly labelled and ribosomal RNA of mammalian cells and *E. coli*. *Nature, Lond.* **222**, 446.

52. TAMAOKI, T. and LANE, B. G. (1967). The chain termini and alkalistable dinucleotide sequences in rapidly labeled ribonucleates from L cells. *Biochemistry, N.Y.* **6**, 3583.

53. GRANBOULAN, N. and SCHERRER, K. (1969). Visualization in the electron microscope and size of RNA from animal cells. *Eur. J. Biochem.* **9**, 1.

54. LUDLUM, D. B. (1966). Methylation and secondary structure of polyadenylic acid. *Biochim. biophys. Acta* **119**, 630.

55. SAPONARA, A. G. and ENGER, M. D. (1966). Incorporation of [^{3}H]-uridine and [Me-^{14}C]methionine into chinese-hamster cell ribonucleic acid. *Biochim. biophys. Acta* **119**, 492.

56. GOLDSTEIN, L. and PLAUT, W. (1955). Direct evidence for nuclear synthesis of cytoplasmic ribose nucleic acid. *Proc. natn. Acad. Sci. U.S.A.* **41**, 874.

57. WATTS, J. W. and HARRIS, H. (1959). Turnover of nucleic acids in a non-multiplying animal cell. *Biochem. J.* **72**, 147.

58. HARRIS, H. (1959). Turnover of nuclear and cytoplasmic ribonucleic acid in two types of animal cell, with some further observations on the nucleolus. *Biochem. J.* **73**, 362.

59. HARRIS, H. and WATTS, J. W. (1962). The relationship between nuclear and cytoplasmic ribonucleic acid. *Proc. R. Soc.* B **156**, 109.

60. WATTS, J. W. (1964). Turnover of nucleic acids in a multiplying animal cell. 2. Retention studies. *Biochem. J.* **93**, 306.

61. SCOTT, J. F., TAFT, E. B., and LETOURNEAU, N. W. (1962). Conservation of nucleic acids by Ehrlich ascites-tumour cells. *Biochim. biophys. Acta* **61**, 62.

62. ADAMS, D. H. (1966). The relationship between cellular nucleic acids in the developing rat cerebral cortex. *Biochem. J.* **98**, 636.

63. HOUSSAIS, J.-F. and ATTARDI, G. (1966). High molecular weight nonribosomal-type nuclear RNA and cytoplasmic messenger RNA in HeLa cells. *Proc. natn. Acad. Sci. U.S.A.* **56**, 616.

64. SCHERRER, K., MARCAUD, L., ZAJDELA, F., BRECKENRIDGE, B., and GROS, F. (1966). Etude des RNA nucléaires et cytoplasmiques à marquage rapide dans les cellules érythropoiétiques aviaires différenciées. *Bull. Soc. Chim. biol.* **48,** 1037.

65. OWEN, M. (1967). Uptake of [^{3}H]uridine into precursor pools and RNA in osteogenic cells. *J. Cell Sci.* **2,** 39.

66. LOEB, J. N., HOWELL, R. R., and TOMKINS, G. M. (1965). Turnover of ribosomal RNA in rat liver. *Science, N.Y.* **149,** 1093.

67. VOLKIN, E. and ASTRACHAN, L. (1956). Phosphorus incorporation in *Escherichia coli* ribonucleic acid after infection with bacteriophage T2. *Virology* **2,** 149.

68. SPENCER, T. (1962). The incorporation of [^{32}P]phosphate into the ribonucleic acid of HeLa cells and its relation to ribonucleic acid base composition. *Biochem. J.* **84,** 87P.

69. MARBAIX, G., BURNY, A., HUEZ, G., and CHANTRENNE, H. (1966). Base composition of messenger RNA from rabbit reticulocytes. *Biochim. biophys. Acta* **114,** 404.

70. HADJIOLOV, A. A., VENKOV, P. V., DOLAPCHIEV, L. B., and GENCHEV, D. D. (1967). The action of snake venom phosphodiesterase on liver ribosomal ribonucleic acids. *Biochim. biophys. Acta* **142,** 111.

71. ELLEM, K. A. O. and SHERIDAN, J. W. (1964). Tenacious binding of the bulk of the DNA-like RNA of metazoan cells to methylated albumin columns. *Biochem. biophys. Res. Commun.* **16,** 505.

72. BRAMWELL, M. E. (1970). Intranuclear accumulation of RNA resembling the smaller ribosomal RNA component. *J. Cell Sci.* **6,** 53.

73. TAMAOKI, T. and LANE, B. G. (1968). Methylation of sugars and bases in ribosomal and rapidly labelled ribonucleates from normal and puromycin-treated L cells. *Biochemistry, N.Y.* **7,** 3431.

74. SCHERRER, K., LATHAM, H., and DARNELL, J. E. (1963). Demonstration of an unstable RNA and of a precursor to ribosomal RNA in HeLa cells. *Proc. natn. Acad. Sci. U.S.A.* **49,** 240.

75. PENMAN, S. (1966). RNA metabolism in the HeLa cell nucleus. *J. molec. Biol.* **17,** 117.

76. WEINBERG, R. A., LOENING, U., WILLEMS, M., and PENMAN, S. (1967). Acrylamide gel electrophoresis of HeLa cell nucleolar RNA. *Proc. natn. Acad. Sci. U.S.A.* **58,** 1088.

77. WEINBERG, R. A. and PENMAN, S. (1970). Processing of 45S nucleolar RNA. *J. molec. Biol.* **47,** 169.

78. ENNIS, H. (1966). Synthesis of RNA in L cells during inhibition of protein synthesis by cycloheximide. *Molec. Pharm.* **2,** 543.

79. WAGNER, E. K. and ROIZMAN, B. (1968). Effect of vinca alkaloids on RNA synthesis in human cells *in vitro. Science, N.Y.* **162,** 569.

80. MAYO, V. S., ANDREAN, B. A. G., and DE KLOET, S. R. (1968). Effects of cycloheximide and 5-fluorouracil on the synthesis of RNA in yeast. *Biochim. biophys. Acta* **169,** 297.

81. ROBERTS, W. K. and D'ARI, L. (1968). Base sequence differences between ribosomal and 'ribosomal precursor' ribonucleic acids from Ehrlich ascites cells. *Biochemistry, N.Y.* **7,** 592.

82. WIKMAN, J., HOWARD, E., and BUSCH, H. (1969). Studies on the primary structure of ribosomal 28S ribonucleic acid and its nucleolar precursors. Isolation of an electrophoretically homogeneous fragment rich in guanylic and cytidylic acids. *J. biol. Chem.* **244**, 5471.

83. MARKS, F., HIDVEGI, E. J., YAZDI, E., and BUSCH, H. (1969). Isotope content of oligonucleotides of nuclear and nucleolar RNA of rat liver. *Biochim. biophys. Acta* **195**, 340.

84. TSANEV, R. G., MARKOV, G. G., and DESSEV, G. N. (1966). Incorporation of labelled precursors into the electrophoretic fractions of rat-liver ribonucleic acid. *Biochem. J.* **100**, 204.

85. BOYADJIEV, S. I. and HADJIOLOV, A. A. (1968). Fractionation and biosynthesis of ribonucleic acid of the rat adrenals. *Biochim. biophys. Acta* **161**, 341.

86. COOPER, H. L. and KAY, J. E. (1969). Differential extraction of nuclear and cytoplasmic RNA from intact lymphocytes. *Biochim. biophys. Acta* **174**, 503.

87. KAY, J. E. and COOPER, H. L. (1969). Rapidly labelled cytoplasmic RNA in normal and phytohaemagglutinin-stimulated human lymphocytes. *Biochim. biophys. Acta* **N31**, 62.

88. BILLING, R. J., INGLIS, A. M., and SMELLIE, R. M. S. (1969). The distribution of deoxyribonucleic acid-like ribonucleic acid in rat liver cells. *Biochem. J.* **113**, 571.

89. HARRIS, H. (1963). The breakdown of RNA in the cell nucleus. *Proc. R. Soc.* B **158**, 79.

90. SCOTT, J. F., KALTREIDER, H. B., BOEKER, F. A., and TAFT, E. B. (1964). Studies on the nuclear RNA of Ehrlich ascites tumour cells. *Fedn Proc. Fedn Am. Socs exp. Biol.* **23**, 168.

91. HARRIS, H. (1965). The short-lived RNA in the cell nucleus and its possible role in evolution. *Evolving genes and proteins* (Eds. V. BRYSON, and H. J. VOGEL), p. 469, Academic Press, New York.

92. EDSTRÖM, J.-E. (1965). Chromosomal RNA and other nuclear RNA fractions. *Role of the chromosomes in development* (Ed. M. LOCKE), p. 137. Academic Press, New York.

93. BRUNS, G. P., FISCHER, S., and LOWY, B. A. (1965). A study of the synthesis and interrelationships of ribonucleic acids in duck erythrocytes. *Biochim. biophys. Acta* **95**, 280.

94. SOEIRO, R., BIRNBOIM, H. C., and DARNELL, J. E. (1966). Rapidly labelled HeLa cell nuclear RNA. *J. molec. Biol.* **19**, 362.

95. LAZARUS, H. M. and SPORN, M. B. (1967). Purification and properties of a nuclear exoribonuclease from Ehrlich ascites tumour cells. *Proc. natn. Acad. Sci. U.S.A.* **57**, 1386.

96. SCHÜTZ, G., GALLWITZ, D., and SEKERIS, C. E. (1968). Rapidly labelled high molecular RNA from rat liver. *Eur. J. Biochem.* **4**, 149.

97. SOEIRO, R., VAUGHAN, M. H., WARNER, J. R., and DARNELL, J. E. (1968). The turnover of nuclear DNA-like RNA in HeLa cells. *J. Cell Biol.* **39**, 112.

98. KIJIMA, S. and WILT, F. H. (1969). Rate of nuclear ribonucleic acid turnover in sea urchin embryos. *J. molec. Biol.* **40**, 235.

99. ARONSON, A. I. and WILT, F. H. (1969). Properties of nuclear RNA in sea urchin embryos. *Proc. natn. Acad. Sci. U.S.A.* **62,** 186.
100. FREEDMAN, M. L., HONIG, G. R., and RABINOWITZ, M. (1966). The role of newly synthesized RNA on nuclear histone synthesis by chicken immature erythrocytes. *Expl Cell Res.* **44,** 263.
101. PONTECORVO, G. (1966). Template and stepwise processes in heredity. *Proc. R. Soc.* B **164,** 167.
102. PLAGEMANN, P. G. W. (1969). RNA synthesis in exponentially growing rat hepatoma cells. I. A caution in equating pulse-labelled polyribosomal RNA with messenger RNA. *Biochim. biophys. Acta* **182,** 46.
103. PERRY, R. P. and KELLEY, D. E. (1966). Buoyant densities of cytoplasmic ribonucleoprotein particles in mammalian cells: distinctive character of ribosome subunits and the rapidly labelled components. *J. molec. Biol.* **16,** 255.
104. SPIRIN, A. S. and NEMER, M. (1965). Messenger RNA in early seaurchin embryos: cytoplasmic particles. *Science, N.Y.* **150,** 214.
105. INFANTE, A. A. and NEMER, M. (1968). Heterogeneous ribonucleoprotein particles in the cytoplasm of sea urchin embryos. *J. molec. Biol.* **32,** 543.
106. SAMEC, J., JACOB, M., and MANDEL, P. (1968). Occurrence of light particles carrying DNA-like RNA in the microsomal fraction of adult rat brain. *Biochim. biophys. Acta* **161,** 377.
107. HENSHAW, E. C. (1968). Messenger RNA in rat liver polyribosomes: evidence that it exists as ribonucleoprotein particles. *J. molec. Biol.* **36,** 401.
108. PERRY, R. P. and KELLEY, D. E. (1968). Messenger RNA-protein complexes and newly synthesized ribosomal subunits: analysis of free particles and components of polyribosomes. *J. molec. Biol.* **35,** 37.
109. BURNY, A., HUEZ, G., MARBAIX, G., and CHANTRENNE, H. (1969). On a messenger ribonucleoprotein complex from rabbit reticulocytes. *Biochim. biophys. Acta* **190,** 228.
110. LAYCOCK, D. G. and HUNT, J. A. (1969). Synthesis of rabbit globin by a bacterial cell-free system. *Nature, Lond.* **221,** 1118.
111. LABRIE, F. (1969). Isolation of an RNA with the properties of haemoglobin messenger. *Nature, Lond.* **221,** 1217.
112. LOCKARD, R. E. and LINGREL, J. B. (1969). The synthesis of mouse hemoglobin β chains in a rabbit reticulocyte cell-free system programmed with mouse reticulocyte 9S RNA. *Biochem. biophys. Res. Commun.* **37,** 204.
113. WARNER, J., RICH, A., and HALL, C. (1962). Electron microscope studies of ribosomal clusters synthesizing haemoglobin. *Science, N.Y.* **138,** 1399.
114. WARNER, J. R., KNOPF, P. M., and RICH, A. (1963). A multiple ribosomal structure in protein synthesis. *Proc. natn. Acad. Sci. U.S.A.* **49,** 122.
115. GIERER, A. (1963). Polypeptide synthesis in *Escherichia coli*. I. Ribosomes and the active complex. *J. molec. Biol.* **6,** 148.
116. RICH, A., WARNER, J. R., and GOODMAN, H. M. (1963). The structure

and function of polyribosomes. *Cold Spring Harb. Symp. quant. Biol.* **28,** 269.

117. FENWICK, M. L. (1968). The effect of ribonuclease on polysomes and ribosomes of bacterial and animal cells. *Biochem. J.* **107,** 481.

118. KAY, D. and FENWICK, M. L. In preparation.

119. MANNER, G. and GOULD, B. S. (1965). Ribosomal aggregates in gamma-globulin synthesis in the rat. *Nature, Lond.* **205,** 670.

120. ZAK, R., NAIR, K. G., and RABINOWITZ, M. (1966). Effect of trypsin on *Escherichia coli* and rabbit reticulocyte ribosomes. *Nature, Lond.* **210,** 169.

121. NAIR, K. G., ZAK, R., and RABINOWITZ, M. (1966). Studies of the effect of proteolytic enzymes on ribosomes and polysomes from reticulocytes and rat liver. *Biochemistry, N.Y.* **5,** 2674.

122. BENEDETTI, E. L., ZWEERS, A., and BLOEMENDAL, H. (1968). Structural aspects of eye lens polyribosomes. *Biochem. J.* **108,** 765.

123. PIATAGORSKY, J. (1968). Ribonuclease and trypsin treatment of ribosomes and polyribosomes from sea urchin eggs. *Biochim. biophys. Acta* **166,** 142.

124. SHELTON, E. and KUFF, E. L. (1966). Substructure and configuration of ribosomes isolated from mammalian cells. *J. molec. Biol.* **22,** 23.

125. VAN ITERSON, W. (1966). The fine structure of the ribonucleoprotein in bacterial cytoplasm. *J. Cell Biol.* **28,** 563.

126. KINGSBURY, E. W. and VOELZ, H. (1968). Structural organization of the ribonucleoprotein in *Escherichia coli. J. Bact.* **95,** 1478.

127. PRONCZUK, A. W., BALIGA, B. S., TRIANT, J. W., and MUNRO, H. N. (1968). Comparison of the effect of amino acid supply on hepatic polysome profiles *in vivo* and *in vitro. Biochim. biophys. Acta* **157,** 204.

128. BALIGA, B. S., PRONCZUK, A. W., and MUNRO, H. N. (1968). Regulation of polysome aggregation in a cell-free system through amino acid supply. *J. molec. Biol.* **34,** 199.

129. SIDRANSKY, H., SARMA, D. S. R., BONGIORNO, M., and VERNEY, E. (1968). Effect of dietary tryptophan on hepatic polyribosomes and protein synthesis in fasted mice. *J. biol. Chem.* **243,** 1123.

130. COHEN, B. B. (1968). A factor converting monoribosomes into polyribosomes during protein synthesis *in vitro. Biochem. J.* **110,** 231.

131. ENNIS, H. L. and SELLS, B. A. (1968). Breakdown and re-formation of polysomes in *Escherichia coli* during inhibition of protein synthesis. *Biochim. biophys. Acta* **161,** 503.

132. MUNRO, A. J., JACKSON, R. J., and KORNER, A. (1963). Studies on the nature of polysomes. *Biochem. J.* **92,** 289.

133. NIRENBERG, M. W. and MATTHAEI, J. H. (1961). The dependence of cell-free protein synthesis in *E. coli* upon naturally occurring or synthetic polyribonucleotides. *Proc. natn. Acad. Sci. U.S.A.* **47,** 1588.

134. NIRENBERG, M., CASKEY, T., MARSHALL, R., BRIMACOMBE, R., KELLOGG, D., DOCTOR, B., HATFIELD, D., LEVIN, J., ROTTMAN, F., PESTKA, S., WILCOX, M., and ANDERSON, F. (1966). The RNA code and protein synthesis. *Cold Spring Harb. Symp. quant. Biol.* **31,** 11.

135. BARONDES, S. H. and NIRENBERG, M. W. (1962). Fate of a synthetic

polynucleotide directing cell-free protein synthesis. I. Characteristics of degradation. *Science, N.Y.* **138,** 810.

136. FENWICK, M. L. (1970) The association of viral RNA with ribosomes in infected bacteria. *J. molec. Biol.* In press.

137. NATHANS, D., NOTANI, G., SCHWARTZ, J. H., and ZINDER, N. D. (1962). Biosynthesis of the coat protein of coliphage f2 by *E. coli* extracts. *Proc. natn. Acad. Sci. U.S.A.* **48,** 1424.

138. SCHWARTZ, J. H., EISENSTADT, J. M., BRAWERMAN, G., and ZINDER, N. D. (1965). Biosynthesis of the coat protein of coliphage f2 by extracts of *Euglena gracilis. Proc. natn. Acad. Sci. U.S.A.* **53,** 195.

139. NATHANS, D. (1965). Cell-free protein synthesis directed by coliphage MS 2 RNA: synthesis of intact viral coat protein and other products. *J. molec. Biol.* **13,** 521.

Additional note (page 57).

28S and 16S are the sedimentation coefficients for the two ribosomal RNA components in animal cells, calculated at infinite dilution. Higher figures, for example 30S and 18S, are sometimes given. These are not more accurate values, but are simply a reflection of what corrections one chooses to make in arriving at the sedimentation coefficient.

4. Regulation

1. Control of 'translation'

An unregenerate 'translationist' like myself soon finds himself faced with the problem of trying to explain how cytoplasmic regulation of protein synthesis might be brought about. It is a source of embarrassment to me that, after having argued at length that protein synthesis is regulated by mechanisms that operate in the cytoplasm of the cell, I am unable to provide any serious body of experimental evidence concerning the precise chemical nature of this regulation. There appear to me to be two reasons for this. The first is that much more effort has been expended in devising and testing models for regulatory process that might operate at the genetic level than in examining cytoplasmic regulatory mechanisms. The second is that we still only have very general and essentially schematic ideas about many aspects of the mechanism of protein synthesis. For example, our textbooks are full of diagrams showing ribosomes rolling along a messenger tape and thus fulfilling their role as a 'read-out' mechanism.[1] But, as I pointed out in Chapter 3, in the cytoplasm of normal cells the 'messenger' tape has proved to be extraordinarily elusive; and I can find no decisive evidence that the ribosomes roll along it. Indeed, both in the intact cytoplasm and in disrupted cell systems there are observations that might make such a scheme rather unlikely. In some cells, especially those involved in the production and secretion of large amounts of specialized proteins, the ribosomes are attached to an elaborate membrane system. This attachment is a very firm one and quite drastic procedures involving dissolution of the membrane are required to release the ribosomes. The ribosomes are disposed as a single layer on one surface of the membranes and may be very closely packed together, rather like a cloth studded with closely set buttons (Plates 2*a* and 2*b*). It has been shown that most of the protein synthesis in the cytoplasm of such cells does indeed take place on these membrane-bound ribosomes,[2] but neither the distribution of the ribosomes on the membrane nor the firmness of their attachment to it encourage the idea that they are busy rolling along hypothetical linear tapes. Moreover, in disrupted cell systems in which the synthesis of polypeptides is specified by added artificial polynucleotides, the small fraction of the added polynucleotide that functions as a template is firmly bound to the ribosomes, and bound in such a way that it is protected from the action of the ribonucleases that abound in disrupted cell preparations.[3] These findings also lend little support to the idea that the ribosomes in such preparations are rolling along a naked extended tape, or, for that matter, that the extended tape is moving over a row of static ribosomes.

I raise these difficulties not in order to point out, once again, how tenuously based some of our current notions are, but to illustrate the difficulty of suggesting precise models for the regulation of protein synthesis when we do not have any clear three-dimensional picture of how this synthesis takes place. Two general models for regulation at the cytoplasmic level are at present being discussed, one involving special forms of transfer RNA, the other configurational changes in the partially synthesized protein. The idea that the translation of the template might be regulated by special forms of transfer RNA appears first to have been suggested by Ames and Hartman[4] to account for the behaviour of 'polarity mutants' at the histidine locus in *Salmonella*. In these mutants, a mutation at one site in the cluster of related genes that controls the biosynthesis of histidine affects the rate of synthesis of the enzymes specified by neighbouring genes in a characteristic way: only the genes distal to the mutation in the direction of DNA transcription are affected, and the enzymes specified by these genes are synthesized in decreasing amounts the further removed the genes are from the site of mutation. Ames and Hartman suggested that there might be special families of transfer RNA ('modulator' transfer ribonucleic acids) that function normally as acceptors of amino acids, but also have the ability to impose a limitation on the rate at which the RNA templates are translated into protein. It was proposed that 'modulator' transfer ribonucleic acids might act either by dislodging the ribosomes from the 'messenger' tape or, by holding up the progress of an active ribosome, dislodge subsequent ones. In the meantime, the tape might be degraded from the distal end, so that, all in all, there would be a decreasing probability of the distal end of the tape being translated. This scheme was further extended by later authors, and rather specific models have been proposed in which 'modulator' or 'analogue' transfer ribonucleic acids form the essential basis of a general mechanism for governing the rate of synthesis of proteins.[5] To explain regulation of enzyme synthesis in statistical terms that involve considerations of the probability of ribosomes being dislodged from the tape[4] is to offer an explanation that is, for my taste, too far removed from present experimental realities. And if this model is further complicated by selective degradation of the tape from one end, all the difficulties that I have already discussed in connection with the general problem of attempting to account for regulation of protein synthesis by selective degradation of templates apply. There is evidence that repression of the enzymes responsible for histidine and valine biosynthesis in Gram-negative organisms may require the formation of histidyl- or valyl-transfer RNA;[6-10] but this does not appear to be the case for phenylalanine or tyrosine biosynthesis.[11,12] And a detailed study of arginine biosynthesis indicates that at least the bulk of the arginyl-transfer RNA is not involved in repression.[13,14] An awkward feature of all general regulatory models involving specialized transfer RNA molecules is the *prima facie* requirement for very large numbers of such molecules. If modulation by transfer RNA is to be a general mechanism for regulating protein synthesis, one might imagine that the number of modulating molecules might approach, or even exceed, the number of templates. We clearly do not have anything like the necessary number of different types of transfer RNA molecules that the simplest statement of this model requires. Stent[5] has pointed out that this difficulty could be overcome if a sextuplet instead of a triplet of nucleotides in the template were involved in specifying the attachment of the 'modulator' transfer RNA, or if both of two different triplets were involved. This is admittedly a possible numerical solution of the difficulty, but it is very much an *ad hoc* argument, and lacks even the beginnings of experimental support.

It has always seemed to me an attractive proposition to suppose that protein synthesis would be regulated by mechanisms that operate at the site of the synthesis itself, and that the specificity of these regulatory mechanisms would in some way reside in the unique ability of proteins to recognize other molecules, both large and small, with a high degree of discrimination. I therefore find schemes that make use of the discriminatory power of proteins more acceptable than those that do not. The simplest of all such schemes, and one that appears to have been first suggested more than a decade ago by Vogel,[15] is that the regulatory mechanisms operate by controlling the release of the polypeptides from the templates on which they are formed. There is no difficulty in envisaging the possibility that the rate of release of polypeptides from their templates can be regulated; indeed there is ample evidence that it is. But the essential requirement of any general model is that it must provide a basis for the specificity of the regulation: it must satisfactorily explain how a metabolizable carbohydrate represses the synthesis of β-galactosidase in *E. coli* and how the availability of haem limits the synthesis of globin in the reticulocyte. This requirement for specificity means that the molecule effecting the regulation and the polypeptide whose synthesis is being regulated must be able to recognize each other while the polypeptide is still attached in some way to the template. If the whole of the polypeptide is synthesized before any part of it can be released from the template, it is difficult to see how this mutual recognition could come about, since the steric specificity of protein molecules resides in their three-dimensional configuration. The possibility must therefore be considered that the polypeptide comes away from the template as synthesis proceeds, and that the freed portion of the polypeptide assumes some measure of specific three-dimensional structure before the whole of the chain is released. In this way the polypeptide may achieve a configuration capable of recognizing some other molecules while it is still attached in part to the template. It can then be supposed that the interaction between the partially completed polypeptide chain and the molecule that it recognizes blocks any further folding and release of the chain from the template.[16]

The plausibility of this model is greatly enhanced by the recent work that has been done on the three-dimensional structure of the enzyme lysozyme.[5] The structure of this enzyme strongly suggests that synthesis and folding of the polypeptide chain do indeed proceed *pari passu*, so that the configuration assumed by the first parts of the chain to be released from the template may guide the pattern of folding of subsequent parts of the chain. It has, moreover, been shown that attachment of an inhibitor to the enzyme produces an alteration in its shape. It is therefore not a far cry to imagine that a molecule may form a specific attachment to a partially formed polypeptide chain and, in doing so, may render further release of the chain impossible. One may thus envisage regulation of the synthesis of the protein operating via an equilibrium between free and attached inhibitor molecules; as the concentration of these molecules in the cell rises, their progressive attachment to the relevant partially formed proteins suppresses further synthesis of these proteins; and when the concentration of inhibitor molecules in the cell falls, synthesis of the relevant proteins is resumed. This model is not merely conjectural. There is a substantial body of evidence that suggests that enzymes are themselves involved in the regulation of their own synthesis.[17] Cases have, for example, been described in which a mutation affecting the feedback-sensitive site of an enzyme also affects repressibility of the synthesis of the enzyme;[18, 19] and single mutations in the structural gene for an enzyme may affect both the catalytic activity of the enzyme and its inducibility or repressibility.[20, 21] These observations are difficult to explain except in terms of a model in which the agent responsible for repression of the synthesis of an enzyme interacts in some way with the nascent enzyme itself. Models that involve interaction with nascent polypeptide chains permit regulation directly by small molecules, or indirectly through the intervention of other proteins. The synthesis of a particular enzyme could be regulated either by direct interaction with substrate or end-product, or by interaction with some other protein that has the ability to recognize, and hence to attach to, the partially formed enzyme. It seems necessary to postulate the existence of mechanisms that would permit a metabolite to regulate the synthesis of a particular protein indirectly, that is, not only by simple attachment of the metabolite to the partially formed protein, because of the great variation that one finds in the lag period that precedes induced enzyme synthesis, when one compares different enzymes and different organisms. Thus, in *E. coli*, the lag for β-galactosidase induction is 2–3 min[22] but for acetylornithine-transaminase it is about 8 min;[23] and for penicillinase in *B. cereus* it is about 10–15 min.[24] In animal cells the lag is usually to be measured in hours. While, in some cases, this lag may be accounted for, at least in part, by the time required to establish an adequate intracellular concentration of the metabolite in question, in other cases this explanation does not apply. Interaction between a metabolite and a protein that recognizes it must occur virtually without lag, so that where there is a lag despite adequate intracellular concentration of the metabolite, it seems probable that the synthesis of the relevant protein is regulated by a more complex chain of events.

2. Control of 'transcription'

I come now to discuss 'genetic regulation' proper, that is to say, regulation of the primary activity of genes, the synthesis of RNA on DNA. In principle, regulation of the transcription of DNA may operate in two ways: by variation in the rate of synthesis of RNA at any one genetic locus, or by variation in the number of active genes. It is, of course, also possible that the intrinsic structure of some genes may dictate a slower rate of transcription than that of other genes. If this were the case, all genetic regulatory phenomena would have to operate on a basis of intrinsically different transcription rates for different genes. We do not at present have any decisive evidence on this point. There is no doubt, however, that genetic activity can be regulated by both of the other mechanisms that have been mentioned: by changes in the over-all rate of RNA transcription and by changes in the amount of DNA transcribed. The over-all rate of RNA synthesis on the genes is, like any other synthetic process, governed by the general energy level in the cell, by the availability of the necessary precursors, and by the concentrations of the enzymes involved. There is no doubt that dramatic and rapid fluctuations in RNA synthesis can occur in response to changes in the environment of the cell, often to quite trivial changes. But this form of regulation does not greatly illuminate the study of gene action. The real centre of interest is in mechanisms that permit *specificity* of genetic regulation, that is, permit the synthesis of RNA on some genes but not on others.

I have already discussed the experiments with bacteria that suggest that single genes or small groups of genes may be switched off by the attachment of specific repressors. Another mechanism that has recently been proposed for the control of transcription involves specificity of interaction between the DNA and the enzyme responsible for its transcription (RNA polymerase). It is clear that some mechanism must exist to ensure that the transcription of a gene begins at the beginning of the gene and ends at the end; if this were not so, the great bulk of the RNA templates produced by the cell would be incomplete or overlapping. There is now good evidence that this chaos is avoided by the provision, at the beginning of each gene or sequence of genes, of a specific region that the RNA polymerase can recognize as a site for the initiation of transcription (for example, the *p* region in the *lac* genes of *E. coli*); and there may also be regions at the ends of some genes that are recognized as sites at which transcription must stop. Some indications of how this recognition might be achieved have recently been obtained by a study of the RNA polymerase of *E. coli*. It appears that this enzyme is composed of two parts: one, known as the 'core enzyme', is thought to be a general RNA polymerase with little substrate specificity; the other, known as the 'sigma factor', apparently ensures the recognition of the genetic regions where transcription is to be initiated.[25] For example, in the absence of the sigma factor, RNA polymerase from *E. coli* will initiate transcription at random sites on the DNA of bacteriophage T4; but when the sigma factor is added, only those genes that are normally expressed during the first minute after infection *in vivo* are transcribed.[26] When the DNA of bacteriophage fd is transcribed by *E. coli* RNA polymerase in the absence of the sigma factor, RNA chains are produced that begin with nucleotides not normally present at the beginning of the RNA chains synthesized *in vivo*; but the addition of the sigma factor greatly reduces the production of such abnormal RNA chains.[27] It is therefore clear that some measure of specificity is conferred on RNA polymerase by its sigma factor; but it is difficult to believe that recognition systems contained in the structure of the RNA polymerase itself could provide a general mechanism for the selective transcription of single genes or small groups of related genes. This would require not only a range of sigma factors comparable in magnitude to the number of genetic units to be transcribed, but also mechanisms for regulating the synthesis of the sigma factors, and co-factors for regulating their attachment to the genes that they recognize. All this would simply amount to another version of the genetic operator model with sigma factors in RNA polymerases as the regulatory units. The difficulty of accommodating all we know about the regulation of protein synthesis in terms of a mechanism that acts only at the level of the DNA is not removed by adding sigma factors to repressors; and the complexity of the model is enormously increased.

What evidence is there for the applicability of the genetic operator model to higher cells? Do we have any indications in such cells that the transcription of single genes or small groups of genes can be selectively suppressed? Here is a list of all the cases known to me in which there is direct evidence of selective suppression of RNA synthesis in eukaryotic cells.

(1) Inactivation of the entire paternal set of chromosomes in the mealy bug, *Pseudococcus obscurus*.[28]

(2) Inactivation of individual sex chromosomes in some species of vertebrates.[29-31]

(3) Inactivation of 'condensed' regions of interphase nuclei in some differentiated somatic cells of animals.[32]

(4) Inactivation of 'unexpanded' bands or segments in the giant polytene chromosomes found in the glandular cells of certain insects.[33, 34]

I do not propose to discuss the general question of the genetic activity of heterochromatic chromosomes, or heterochromatic segments of chromosomes, as identified in metaphase preparations. It is now clear that many of these heterochromatic segments do contain genes that produce identifiable phenotypic effects, but we do not know in the vast majority of cases whether these segments synthesize RNA throughout interphase, as appears to be the case for the heterochromatic regions responsible for the formation of the nucleolus; whether they synthesize RNA only at certain specified times; or whether, like the heterochromatic X chromosomes, they are very largely inactive. I am therefore obliged to limit my discussion to the four cases in which there actually is direct evidence of total or partial suppression of RNA synthesis. The conclusions that I shall draw thus inevitably rest on a very slender body of observation.†

The inactivation of the paternal set of chromosomes in the mealy bug and the inactivation of one of the X chromosomes in certain vertebrates appear to me to be incomplete manifestations of a more widespread phenomenon, namely, the complete elimination of some or all of the chromosomes of either the paternal or the maternal set. In the fungus gnat, *Sciara*, for example, the whole paternal set of chromosomes is eliminated in the male, which thus functions with only a maternal set of chromosomes.[35] In other related forms, the males develop from unfertilized eggs and thus contain only the maternal chromosomes.[36] It seems very likely that the inactivation of the paternal set of chromosomes in the mealy bug is simply another means of achieving the same end, and it is possible that inactivation is an evolutionary alternative to complete elimination. A similar argument probably holds for the inactivation of one of the X chromosomes in the females of certain vertebrates. In some insects, one or other of the sex chromosomes is normally eliminated early in development,[37] and a similar situation also exists in certain mammals[38] and marsupials[39,40] in which the female develops with only one X chromosome. It again appears likely that inactivation, but retention, of the X represents an evolutionary alternative to its complete elimination.

It is, I think, obvious that these two cases of selective suppression of RNA synthesis can have nothing to do with cytoplasmic regulatory phenomena of the sort that I have been discussing in previous chapters. The inactivation of these chromosomes is usually permanent, and it may be virtually complete; it occurs, with minor exceptions, in all tissues of the

† In the first edition of this book, I refrained from discussing any of the results obtained by the technique of DNA-RNA hybridization in higher cells, because I felt that the validity of this technique for higher cells had not been established. Subsequent work has confirmed this view.[106-109] In my judgement, the results obtained by this technique in higher cells still cannot be interpreted with confidence.

body; and it involves only one of the two homologous chromosomes or chromosome sets. This form of chromosomal inactivation may have great evolutionary and ontogenetic significance, but it is difficult to conceive how it could play any direct role in controlling the rates of synthesis of individual cytoplasmic proteins.

Although a direct demonstration has been made in very few cell types, it is probable that other highly condensed heterochromatic or heteropyknotic regions in interphase nuclei also synthesize very much less RNA than the euchromatic regions. In certain highly differentiated cells, the process of differentiation involves a marked reduction in nuclear volume, and this is accompanied by visible condensation of large parts of the chromatin. In these condensed regions RNA synthesis is suppressed, and in some cases the nucleus may stop synthesizing RNA altogether. This process is best seen in the differentiation of the red blood cells in certain vertebrates, where progressive condensation of the chromatin is associated with progressive reduction of RNA synthesis as the cell assumes specialized morphological characteristics.[41] This form of nuclear differentiation appears to be a means of imposing a state of dormancy, or even reproductive death, on the specialized cell. Where the effect is reversible, as in the small lymphocyte or the fibrocyte of vertebrates, the cell nucleus enlarges again, and the condensed chromatin within it becomes dispersed, when the dormant cell resumes a high level of metabolic activity. Complete inactivation of the nucleus again appears to be an evolutionary alternative to its elimination: in mammals the whole nucleus is eliminated during differentiation of the erythrocyte;[42] in amphibians, birds, reptiles, and some other orders, the nucleus is retained but appears to be completely inactive.

Cells that are not in the process of becoming dormant may contain smaller condensed regions of chromatin (chromocentres) in addition to the one produced by the inactivated X chromosome.[43,44] These may represent the heterochromatic segments that are seen in the chromosomes at metaphase, but this has not, in general, been established. It is not unlikely that these chromocentres will also be found to synthesize little or no RNA, but, as far as I am aware, the experiment has not yet been done. Chromocentres may persist throughout the whole

life of a cell, or they may be formed only at certain stages in
the cell cycle; in any one tissue or organ, they may not be
present in all cells of the same type. Even the smallest chromo-
centre would involve the inactivation of a huge number of
individual genes. We do not, at present, have any precise information about the phenotypic consequences of this piecemeal
inactivation of the genetic material. The important question is,
of course, whether the suppression of RNA synthesis produced
by this mechanism is a means of achieving the differentiation of
the specialized cell, or whether it is a consequence of the specialization. I shall argue in a later chapter in support of the second
alternative. In the present context, it is enough to say that this
form of genetic inactivation, although it may, in some cases,
affect areas smaller than a whole chromosome, is still too gross
a process to form a basis for regulating the synthesis of specific
cytoplasmic proteins.

3. Puffs in polytene chromosomes

We now come to the one case that does, at least at first sight,
appear to provide an adequate structural basis for the genetic
operator model of protein synthesis: the giant polytene chromosomes of certain insects. These chromosomes are found in the
larvae of many *Diptera* in the cells of glandular tissues, especially
those derived from the gut. The salivary glands have been most
extensively studied. The chromosomes in these glands are
extraordinary for two reasons. The first is that they are grossly
polytenic. Each chromosome contains thousands of identical
parallel copies of the basic diploid genetic structure. The extent
of polyteny may vary in different species, but for *Chironomus
tentans* it has been estimated that each chromosome contains
about 16 000 times the normal diploid amount of DNA.[45] This
accounts for the huge size of these chromosomes and for the
fact that structural details (vastly magnified by the existence of
the polyteny) can be made out in them that cannot be resolved in normal diploid material. Not all the genes in the basic
diploid set are apparently replicated to the same extent; it
appears that the heterochromatic segments of the normal diploid chromosomes do not take part in the process of polytenization and thus have a minimal representation in the giant
chromosomes.[46] The second unusual feature of these chromo-

somes is that they are visible as discrete condensed entities throughout a large part of the life cycle of the cell. Their physiological state thus resembles a protracted and, since the cell does not divide, abortive prophase. It is difficult to know how far the observations made on the physiology of these extraordinary chromosomes can be extrapolated to normal diploid cells, but, if extrapolation is possible, the conditions that appear to provide the closest parallel are those stages of mitotic prophase in which the chromosomes are already condensed into discrete units, but in which some synthesis of RNA none the less takes place.

The bulk of the genetic material in the giant chromosomes is inactive. There are about 2000 identifiable (DNA) bands in the whole chromosome set in *Drosophila* and perhaps 5000 in *Chironomus*, but only about 300 of these bands have at any time been observed to synthesize RNA or to form 'puffs', the characteristic morphological change that the bands undergo when they are activated[33] (Plate 3a). The maximum number of loci that are active simultaneously is less than this: not more than about 200 bands have been seen to synthesize RNA at any one time. Measurements of the DNA content of the individual bands indicates that a band of average dimensions represents the polytenization of a primary unit that contains enough DNA to account for about 100 genes,[45] and many bands, of course, contain much more than the average amount of DNA. We are therefore dealing, even in these chromosomes, with the activation and inactivation of relatively large units of the genetic material. The activation of these units depends upon the existence of polyteny. The synthesis of RNA in each active band is controlled by the formation of a puff in which increasing numbers of identical polytenic copies of the same basic genetic unit are opened up and thus become accessible to the transcription machinery (Plate 3b). The degree of activity of each genetic unit is therefore determined by the number of polytenic copies that are available for transcription. It is difficult to see how a control mechanism that depends upon a polytenic chromosomal structure could operate in chromosomes that are not polytenic. If, in normal diploid cells, the two strands of the DNA helix came apart when the DNA was transcribed, the process might be regarded as analogous to 'puffing'; but we do not have any evidence that the two strands of the DNA do come apart during transcription, and such a process would not, in any case, provide a mechanism for regulating the amount of RNA produced at any one locus, as 'puffing' appears to do.

It has been contended that the pattern of puffing shows organ specificity,[47] but the evidence for this does not seem to be conclusive. It does indeed happen that the pattern of puffing may be different in the chromosomes of different tissues, but this pattern varies from animal to animal in the cells of any one tissue, and also varies with the physiological state and the stage of development of the larva. When the physiological variation in puffing pattern is taken into account, very few, if any, puffs are found to be tissue-specific in the sense that they are found only in one particular tissue.[48] Some loci are found to be puffed throughout most stages of development, but others are puffed only at certain specific stages.[33, 34, 48] In the salivary glands, the most intense puffing activity, is seen just before the moulting periods, especially before the pupal moult during which meta-morphosis occurs and the salivary glands break down. The puffing pattern associated with the pupal moult may persist even when the cells of the salivary glands have begun to undergo autolysis.

The phenotypic consequences of these various puffing patterns are far from clear, but it seems unlikely that puffing can be an immediate determinant for regulating the synthesis of individual cytoplasmic proteins. The genetic unit involved in puffing is too large to be responsible for the control of a single protein, or even for the co-ordinate regulation of a group of related proteins, unless, in *Diptera*, these groups are an order of magnitude, or more, larger than they are in bacteria. As I have already pointed out, only 200 to 300 bands are subject to puffing, and of these, many are more or less continuously puffed. There is evidence that in the salivary gland some of the puffs are involved in determining the synthesis of secretory proteins,[49-52] although it appears that many of the proteins of the salivary secretion are not synthesized in the gland, but are simply extracted from the haemolymph.[53] Some of the puffs in the giant cells of the foot pad of the fly appear to be involved in determining the secretion and maturation of the cuticle.[34]

The intense puffing activity associated with the moults has suggested the idea that some puffs might provide templates for the synthesis of the enzymes or enzyme-containing 'lysosomes' that destroy the gland at metamorphosis;[54, 55] and the possibility has also been considered that the puffs might be responsible for the production of substances that are required after metamorphosis. There is, of course, no reason why some of the RNA made in the puffs should not carry information for the synthesis of specific proteins; but the idea that the appearance and disappearance of a particular puff determine the onset and cessation of synthesis of a particular protein, in the manner proposed by the genetic operator model, is very difficult to accept. Even when the synthesis of RNA in the salivary glands of *Chironomns tentans* has been inhibited for 48 hours by the administration of actinomycin D, salivary proteins continue to be synthesized at the normal rate; and the specific cell granules associated with the salivary secretion in *Chironomus pallidivittatus* continue to be formed under these conditions.[56, 57] The secretion of albumin by the salivary glands is also insensitive to the suppression of RNA synthesis by actinomycin D.[58] The regulation of protein synthesis in the cells of these glands thus conforms to the general pattern that we have seen in *Acetabularia* and other higher cells, despite the formation of chromosomal puffs.

4. The mechanisms that govern transcription

We have now to consider the mechanisms by which localized suppression of RNA synthesis in the chromosomes of eukaryotic cells is brought about. The genetic operator model of protein synthesis postulates a very high order of precision in the regulatory mechanisms which operate at the genetic level: single genes or small groups of genes are switched on and off. This type of model requires that the signals which pass from the cytoplasm to the genes must have a corresponding degree of specificity. They must be able to recognize one gene from another. Jacob and Monod envisage the existence of an extensive range of specific cytoplasmic molecules (repressors) that are able to recognize specific genetic loci, and, by attaching to these loci, to inhibit their transcription. In the case of coordinate regulation of a contiguous group of genes, the repressor molecule inhibits the transcription of a small number of neighbouring genes as well. None of the examples of localized suppression of transcription that have been described in higher cells appear to be produced in this way. Where a complete haploid set of chromosomes or one of the sex chromosomes is inactivated, it is clear that, if cytoplasmic signals are involved, they do not discriminate between one genetic locus and another, but must operate at an altogether different level. In the one case, the signals must merely distinguish between the paternal and the maternal set of chromosomes as a whole; and the inactivation of the paternal set cannot be due to the cumulative activity of a whole range of specific genetic repressors, since the great bulk of the genetic material is identical in both maternal and paternal chromosome sets. In the case of sex chromosome inactivation, the proposed cytoplasmic signals do not even distinguish between the paternal and the maternal X chromsome. Except in certain special cases,[59, 60] either one or other X chromosome is inactivated at random, and where there are more than two X chromosomes, all except one are inactivated.[31] The control mechanism obviously operates to ensure that not more than one X chromosome shall remain active, and it is not concerned with discriminating between one gene and another. Indeed, translocations involving the X chromosome show decisively that inactivation of this chromosome does not involve a mechanism that recognizes the genes within the chromosome. When a fragment of a normally inactivated X chromosome is translocated into an active autosomal region, the translocated fragment is not inactivated;[61, 62] and when a fragment from a normally active autosome is translocated into an inactive X chromosome, the autosomal fragment is inactivated.[63, 64] It is clear that the inactivation mechanism is not concerned with what these genes are, but where they are.

The condensation and apparent inactivation of large areas of chromatin during the terminal differentiation of certain specialized vertebrate cells appears to be connected with progressive reduction in the volume of the nucleus; and the appearance of smaller chromocentres in cells not undergoing terminal differentiation also appears to be related in some way to nuclear volume.[41, 65, 66] In these cases also, there can be little doubt that any cytoplasmic signals that might be operative act by ensuring

PLATE 9

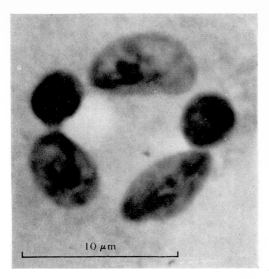

a. A heterokaryon containing three rabbit macrophrage nuclei and two rat lymphocyte nuclei, which are smaller and stain more deeply. Note the peripheral distribution of the nuclei in the cell. (From Harris *et al.*[4] (chap. 5).)

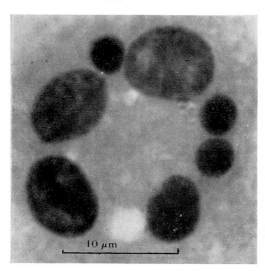

b. A heterokaryon containing four rabbit macrophage nuclei and three hen erythrocyte nuclei. Note the peripheral distribution of the nuclei in the cell. (From Harris *et al.*[4] (chap. 5).)

PLATE 10

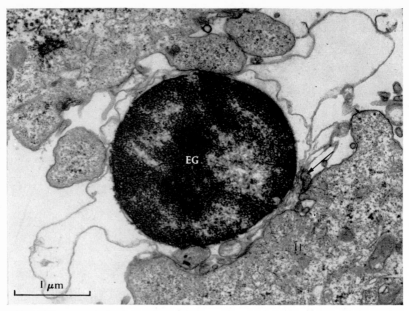

a. An erythrocyte ghost (EG) adherent to a HeLa cell (H). The arrow shows a virus particle wedged between the two cell membranes. (From Schneeberger and Harris[8] (chap. 5).)

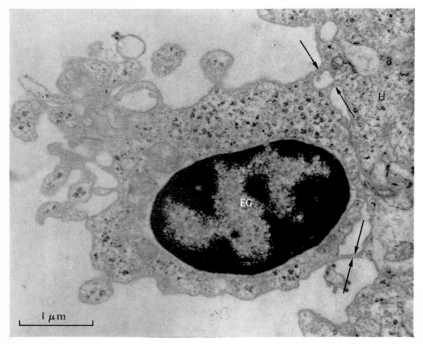

b. Tenuous cytoplasmic bridges, shown by arrows, formed between an erythrocyte ghost (EG) and a HeLa cell (H). The cytoplasm of the HeLa cell, which can be distinguished by its characteristic array of ribosomes, has flowed into the erythrocyte ghost. (From Schneeberger and Harris[8] (chap. 5).)

PLATE 11

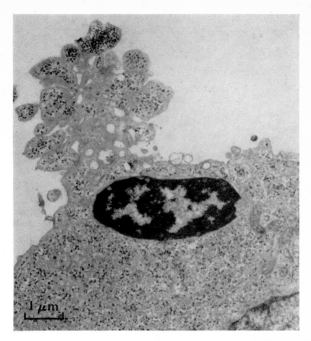

a. An erythrocyte nucleus passing into the cytoplasm of a HeLa cell. (From Schneeberger and Harris[8] (chap. 5).)

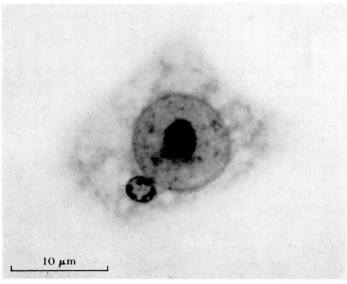

b. A heterokaryon containing one HeLa nucleus and one hen erythrocyte nucleus. The erythrocyte nucleus is highly contracted and its chromatin is condensed. 'Nuclear bodies', which are areas of extreme condensation in the chromatin, are seen. (From Harris[21] (chap. 5).)

PLATE 12

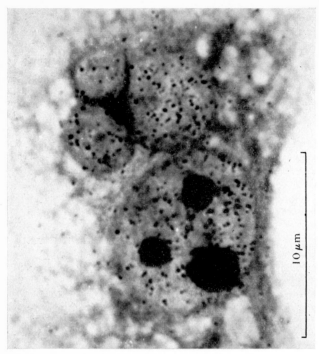

b

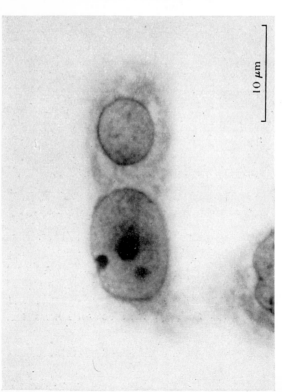

a

a. A heterokaryon containing one HeLa nucleus and one hen erythrocyte nucleus 24 hours after cell fusion. The erythrocyte nucleus has undergone enlargement, the chromatin has become more dispersed and the 'nuclear bodies' are no longer visible. (From Harris[21] (chap. 5).)

b. Autoradiograph of a heterokaryon exposed for 20 min to [³H] uridine. The cell contains one HeLa nucleus and three hen erythrocyte nuclei in various stages of enlargement. All the nuclei are synthesizing RNA. Note that the labelling of the erythrocyte nuclei increases as they enlarge.

the wholesale closure of very large areas of contiguous chromatin and not by inactivating single genes or small clusters of genes.

Some evidence concerning the nature of the mechanisms
that underlie selective condensation of different parts of the
chromatin has recently been provided by the work of Kroeger
and his associates.[67, 68] These workers have shown that the
puffing patterns in dipteran polytene chromosomes do not depend upon the flow of *specific* cytoplasmic signals. Nuclei that
were divested of virtually all their cytoplasm by microsurgical
procedures none the less retained their ability to produce
specific puffing patterns;[67, 69] and replacement of most of the
cytoplasm of a cell of one type with cytoplasm from a cell of a
different type, showing a different puffing pattern, failed to
induce any specific changes in the puffing pattern of the
recipient cell.[70, 71] Removal of the major part of a chromosome
by surgical means did not significantly alter the puffing pattern
of the remaining fragment. These experiments suggest not only
that the puffing patterns are not determined by the flow of
specific repressors from the cytoplasm, but also that they are not
determined by specific signals from one part of the nucleus to
another. It appears that the polytene chromosomes are sensitive
to the movement of water and electrolytes across the nuclear
membrane, and that the specificity of the puffing pattern is
determined, at least in part, by the differential susceptibility of
different parts of the chromosome to changes in osmotic pres-
sure and in the ambient concentrations of specific cations.[72–74]
Moreover, Loewenstein and Kanno[75, 76] have shown that the
nuclear membrane in these salivary gland cells, despite the
apparent 'pores', does constitute a barrier to the free movement
of ions. A strong case can therefore be made in support of the
view that the puffing patterns in these polytene chromosomes are
a reflection of the interaction of the chromosomes with charged
ions that determine the state of condensation or dispersion of
the chromatin at any particular locus. The specificity of the
puffing pattern, on this view, does not reside in the specificity of
the signals that reach the chromosome, but in the structure of
the chromosome itself, which imposes on different loci a differential susceptibility to changes in electrolyte environment.
Although a direct experimental approach to this problem has,
for technical reasons, been limited to these large dipteran cells,

8—N.C.

Siebert and his colleagues[77,78] have now clearly established that
in the somatic cells of vertebrates the electrolyte concentrations
within the nucleus are quite different from those in the cell
cytoplasm; and Ringertz and Bolund[79] have shown that the
initial cytochemical changes that the chromatin of the erythrocyte nucleus undergoes when it is reactivated by cell fusion (see
Chapter 5) can be reproduced in the isolated erythrocyte
nucleus by procedures that remove divalent cations. It therefore
seems to me to be likely that the selective condensation of parts
of the chromatin that one finds in interphase nuclei in most
cells will prove to be a reflection of the differential susceptibility of different parts of the chromatin to changes in the
ambient electrolyte environment.

All this shows very little resemblance to the highly specific
circuits envisaged in the genetic operator model, and, indeed,
argues against the widespread operation of such circuits in
higher cells. For, if so much of the genetic material is subject to
repression on a gross scale by mechanisms with a relatively low
order of specificity, the scope for mechanisms having a high
order of specificity must be limited. In considering any possible
homology between the forms of genetic regulation that can be
observed in higher cells and any similar processes that might
exist in bacteria, one important fact must be taken into account.
If the selective condensation of the chromatin in higher cells
does indeed depend upon changes in electrolyte concentrations
within the nucleus, it is not easy to see how any comparable
mechanisms could operate in bacteria where there is no nuclear
membrane and where the DNA is not bound to structural
protein, as it is in the chromatin of higher forms. There are, I
think, no good grounds for supposing that anything resembling
the phenomena that I have been discussing in higher cells exists
in bacteria.

5. Control of the flow of information from the nucleus

Apart from the regulation of transcription and translation,
there are three other ways in which the expression of genetic
information could be governed in higher cells. There could be
mechanisms that regulate the release of templates from the
DNA, mechanisms that regulate the passage of the templates
across the nuclear membrane, and mechanisms that select for

transport to the cytoplasm only a proportion of the templates made on the DNA. It has been suggested from studies in bacteria that the acts of translation and transcription are closely coupled: more specifically, that when a template ceases to be translated it automatically ceases to be produced.[5] In disrupted bacterial preparations, electron micrographs show that the ribosomes become attached to the DNA when it is transcribed;[80] and labelling experiments confirm that the RNA synthesized on the DNA in such preparations is transferred to the ribosomes.[81] These observations have naturally lent support to the idea that in bacteria the ribosomes might be instrumental in detaching the templates from the DNA. As far as higher cells are concerned, this idea can hardly be entertained. The nucleus of higher cells contains very few, if any, completed ribosomes;[82-85] and those structures which might on morphological grounds be classed as some form of ribosome appear to be limited to the nucleolar areas.[86] There is no evidence for the existence of any appreciable number of completed ribosomes in close proximity to the bulk of the chromatin. While there is no reason to doubt that the rate of release of the RNA from the chromosome may be influenced by a variety of factors, there is, as far as I am aware, no information that suggests that there is anything selective about the mechanism of release. Any locus at which the release of RNA is inhibited is *ipso facto* one at which further transcription is inhibited; so that any model that postulates a highly selective inhibition of the release of templates also postulates a highly selective inhibition of transcription. All that I have said about the specificity of the mechanisms that regulate transcription in higher cells thus applies equally well to any mechanisms that might regulate the release of the templates. It is possible that there may be local variations in the rate of release of RNA from the chromosomes in different parts of the nucleus; but inhibition of the release of templates can hardly be a general mechanism for regulating the expression of the genes. If it were, then inactive genes would have RNA attached to them as well as active genes. But measurement of the ratio of DNA to RNA in the nuclei of higher cells indicates that most of the DNA cannot have RNA attached to it.[87]

Since it now appears that in at least some somatic cells the nuclear membrane is not freely permeable to electrolytes, it is difficult to see how it could be freely permeable to RNA in solution. There is therefore every reason to suppose that there are specific transport mechanisms for the carriage of RNA across the nuclear membrane. With the possible exception of those families of RNA that sediment in the region of the transfer RNA, the cytoplasm of the cell does not contain any RNA free in solution; so that we may envisage the transport of RNA across the nuclear membrane as a complex process involving the passage of RNA that is already linked to protein or acquires its protein as it passes across the membrane. I have already indicated that, in my view, the limiting step in the transfer of information from nucleus to cytoplasm is not the synthesis of the template, but its incorporation into a structure that confers protection from intranuclear degradation; and I have suggested that intranuclear RNA turnover, which apparently takes place, at varying rates, in all cells,[45, 88–96] represents the elimination within the nucleus of those templates that fail to become 'engaged' in this way. In the following chapter I shall propose a more precise model for the mechanism of information transfer and shall present some evidence in support of it.

6. Regulation by means of enzyme degradation

Because there is little turnover of protein in bacteria during exponential growth,[97–99] the possibility that enzyme levels might be regulated by mechanisms that govern the rate of enzyme degradation has, until very recently, been given scant attention. But in bacteria that are not growing exponentially and in metazoan cells, which grow exponentially only in exceptional circumstances, substantial turnover of protein does take place.[100–103] In animal cells, decisive evidence has now been obtained that intracellular enzyme concentrations can be determined by variations not only in the rate of enzyme synthesis but also in the rate of enzyme breakdown. The most detailed studies of this question are those of Schimke and his colleagues on arginase and tryptophan pyrrolase levels in liver cells.[104, 105] These enzymes undergo an easily measurable turnover within the cell and, in both cases, the intracellular enzyme level rises when the substrate of the enzyme, arginine or tryptophan, is supplied. Schimke and his colleagues have shown that the increase in enzyme level produced by the administration of substrate is due in large part to a reduction in the rate of enzyme degradation: the enzyme is stabilized by its substrate. It seems probable that stabilization by substrate will prove to be a phenomenon of quite general importance in the regulation of enzyme levels in higher cells, for an interaction of this sort provides an additional control mechanism that is not only completely specific, but also highly flexible.

REFERENCES

1. WATSON, J. D. (1965). *Molecular biology of the gene*, p. 332. Benjamin, New York.
2. SIEKEVITZ, P. and PALADE, G. E. (1966). Distribution of newly synthesized amylase in microsomal subfractions of guinea pig pancreas. *J. Cell Biol.* **30,** 519.
3. BARONDES, S. H. and NIRENBERG, M. W. (1962). Fate of a synthetic polynucleotide directing cell-free protein synthesis. I. Characteristics of degradation. *Science, N.Y.* **138,** 810.
4. AMES, B. N. and HARTMAN, P. E. (1963). The histidine operon. *Cold Spring Harb. Symp. quant. Biol.* **28,** 349.
5. STENT, G. S. (1964). The operon: on its third anniversary. *Science, N.Y.* **144,** 816.
6. SCHLESINGER, S. and MAGASANIK, B. (1964). Effect of α-methylhistidine on the control of histidine synthesis. *J. molec. Biol.* **9,** 670.
7. ROTH, J. R., ANTON, D. N., and HARTMAN, P. E. (1966). Histidine regulatory mutants in *Salmonella typhimurium*. I. Isolation and general properties. *J. molec. Biol.* **22,** 305.
8. ROTH, J. R. and AMES, B. N. (1966). Histidine regulatory mutants in *Salmonella typhimurium*. II. Histidine regulatory mutants having altered histidyl-tRNA synthetase. *J. molec. Biol.* **22,** 325.
9. SILBERT, D. F., FINK, G. R., and AMES, B. N. (1966). Histidine regulatory mutants in *Salmonella typhimurium*. III. A class of regulatory mutants deficient in tRNA for histidine. *J. molec. Biol.* **22,** 335.
10. EIDLIC, L. and NEIDHARDT, F. C. (1965). Role of valyl-sRNA synthetase in enzyme repression. *Proc. natn. Acad. Sci. U.S.A.* **53,** 539.
11. RAVEL, J. M., WHITE, M. N., and SHIVE, W. (1965). Activation of tyrosine analogs in relation to enzyme repression. *Biochem. biophys. Res. Commun.* **20,** 352.
12. NEIDHARDT, F. C. (1966). Roles of amino acid activating enzymes in cellular physiology. *Bact. Rev.* **30,** 701.
13. HIRSHFIELD, I. N., DeDEKEN, R., HORN, P. C., HOPWOOD, D. A., and MAAS, W. K. (1968). Studies on the mechanism of repression of arginine biosynthesis in *Escherichia coli*. *J. molec. Biol.* **35,** 83.
14. LEISINGER, T. and Vogel, H. J. (1969). Repression by arginine in

Escherichia coli: a comparison of arginyl transfer RNA profiles. *Biochim. biophys. Acta* **182,** 572.

15. VOGEL, H. J. (1957). Repression and induction as control mechanisms of enzyme biogenesis: the 'adaptive' formation of acetylornithinase. *The chemical basis of heredity* (Eds. W. D. McELROY and B. GLASS), p. 276. Johns Hopkins Press, Baltimore, U.S.A.

16. GRUBER, M. and CAMPAGNE, R. N. (1965). Regulation of protein synthesis: an alternative to the repressor-operator hypothesis. *Proc. K. ned. Akad. Wet.* Series C **68,** 1.

17. CLINE, A. L. and BOCK, R. M. (1966). Translational control of gene expression. *Cold Spring Harb. Symp. quant. Biol.* **31,** 321.

18. SOMERVILLE, R. L. and YANOFSKY, C. (1965). Studies on the regulation of tryptophan biosynthesis in *Escherichia coli. J. molec. Biol.* **11,** 747.

19. KOVACH, J. S., BERBERICH, M. A., VENETIANER, P., and GOLDBERGER, R. F. (1969). Repression of the histidine operon: effect of the first enzyme on the kinetics of repression. *J. Bact.* **97,** 1283.

20. BERBERICH, M. and GOTS, J. (1965). A structural gene mutation in *Salmonella typhimurium* resulting in repressibility of adenylosuccinase. *Proc. natn. Acad. Sci. U.S.A.* **54,** 1254.

21. HILL, C. W. and ECHOLS, H. (1966). Properties of a mutant blocked in inducibility of mRNA for the galactose operon of *E. coli. J. molec. Biol.* **19,** 38.

22. PARDEE, A. B. and PRESTIDGE, L. S. (1961). The initial kinetics of enzyme induction. *Biochim. biophys. Acta* **49,** 77.

23. VOGEL, R. H. and VOGEL, H. J. (1965). Onset of repression and derepression in arginine path of *Bacillus subtilis*: a delayed-action 'switch'. *Biochem. biophys. Res. Commun.* **18,** 768.

24. POLLOCK, M. R. (1952). Penicillinase adaptation in *Bacillus cereus*: an analysis of three phases in the response of logarithmically growing cultures to induction of penicillinase formation by penicillin. *Br. J. exp. Path.* **33,** 587.

25. BURGESS, R. R., TRAVERS, A. A., DUNN, J. J., and BAUTZ, E. K. F. (1969). Factor stimulating transcription by RNA polymerase. *Nature, Lond.* **221,** 43.

26. BAUTZ, E. K. F., BAUTZ, F. A., and DUNN, J. J. (1969). *E. coli* σ factor: a positive control element in phage T_4 development. *Nature, Lond.* **223,** 1022.

27. SUGIURA, M., OKAMOTO, T., and TAKANAMI, M. (1970). RNA polymerase σ-factor and the selection of initiation site. *Nature, Lond.* **225,** 598.

28. BERLOWITZ, L. (1965). Correlation of genetic activity, heterochromatization, and RNA metabolism. *Proc. natn. Acad. Sci. U.S.A.* **53,** 68.

29. EVANS, H. J., FORD, C. E., LYON, M. F., and GRAY, J. (1965). DNA replication and genetic expression in female mice with morphologically distinguishable X chromosomes. *Nature, Lond.* **206,** 900.

30. COMINGS, D. E. (1966). Uridine-5-^{3}H radioautography of the human sex chromatin body. *J. Cell Biol.* **28,** 437.

31. HAMERTON, J. L. (1968). Significance of sex chromosome derived heterochromatin in mammals. *Nature, Lond.* **219,** 910.

32. LITTAU, V. C., ALLFREY, V. G., FRENSTER, J. H., and MIRSKY, A. E. (1964). Active and inactive regions of nuclear chromatin as revealed by electron microscope autoradiography. *Proc. natn. Acad. Sci. U.S.A.* **52,** 93.

33. PELLING, C. (1964). Ribonukleinsäure-Synthese der Riesenchromosomen. *Chromosoma* **15,** 71.

34. WHITTEN, J. M. (1969). Coordinated development in the foot pad of the fly *Sarcophaga bullata* during metamorphosis: changing puffing patterns of the giant cell chromosomes. *Chromosoma* **26,** 215.

35. CROUSE, H. V. (1943). Translocations in *Sciara*. Their bearing on chromosome behavior and sex determination. *Univ. Missouri agric. expl Stn Res. Bull.* No. 379, p. 1.

36. BROWN, S. W. (1964). Automatic frequency response in the evolution of male haploidy and other coccid chromosome systems. *Genetics, Princeton* **49,** 797.

37. SWANSON, C. P. (1958). *Cytology and cytogenetics*, pp. 331–5. Macmillan, London.

38. OHNO, S., JAINCHILL, J., and STENIUS, C. (1963). The creeping vole (*Microtus oregoni*) as a gonosomic mosaic. I. The OY/XY constitution of the male. *Cytogenetics* **2,** 232.

39. HAYMAN, D. L. and MARTIN, P. G. (1965). Sex chromosome mosaicism in the marsupial genera isoodon and perameles. *Genetics, Princeton* **52,** 1201.

40. HAYMAN, D. L., MARTIN, P. G., and WALLER, P. F. (1969). Parallel mosaicism of supernumerary chromosomes and sex chromosomes in *Echymipera kalabu* (Marsupialia). *Chromosoma* **27,** 371.

41. CAMERON, I. L. and PRESCOTT, D. M. (1963). RNA and protein metabolism in the maturation of the nucleated chicken erythrocyte. *Expl Cell Res.* **30,** 609.

42. SKUTELSKY, E. and DANON, D. (1967). An electron microscopic study of nuclear elimination from the late erythroblast. *J. Cell Biol.* **33,** 625.

43. MITTWOCH, U. (1967). Barr bodies in relation to DNA values and nuclear size in cultured human cells. *Cytogenetics* **6,** 38.

44. ABERCROMBIE, M. and STEPHENSON, E. M. (1969). Observations on chromocentres in cultured mouse cells. *Nature, Lond.* **222,** 1250.

45. EDSTRÖM, J.-E. (1965). Chromosomal RNA and other nuclear RNA fractions. *Role of the chromosomes in development* (Ed. M. LOCKE), p. 137. Academic Press, New York.

46. RUDKIN, G. T. (1965). Nonreplicating DNA in giant chromosomes. *Genetics, Princeton* **52,** 470.

47. BEERMANN, W. (1952). Chromomerenkonstanz und spezifische Modifikationen der Chromosomenstruktur in der Entwicklung und Organdifferenzierung von *Chironomus tentans. Chromosoma* **5,** 139.

48. CLEVER, U. (1966). Gene activity patterns and cellular differentiation. *Am. Zoologist* **6,** 33.

49. BEERMANN, W. (1961). Ein Balbiani-Ring als Locus einer Speichel-drüsen-mutation. *Chromosoma* **12**, 1.
50. PANITZ, R. (1967). Funktionelle Veränderungen an Riesenchromo-somen nach Behandlung mit Giberellinen. *Biol. Zbl.* **86**, Suppl., p. 147.
51. BAUDISCH, W. and PANITZ, R. (1968). Kontrolle eines biochemischen Merkmals in den Speicheldrüsen von *Acricotopus lucidus* durch einen Balbiani-Ring. *Expl. Cell Res.* **49**, 470.
52. GROSSBACH, U. (1968). Cell differentiation in the salivary glands of *Camptochironomus tentans* and *C. pallidivittatus*. *Annls zool. Fenn.* **5**, 37.
53. DOYLE, D. and LAUFER, H. (1969). Sources of larval salivary gland secretion in the dipteran *Chironomus tentans*. *J. Cell Biol.* **40**, 61.
54. LAUFER, H. and NAKASE, Y. (1965). Developmental studies of the dipteran salivary gland. II. DNAase activity in *Chironomus thummi*. *J. Cell Biol.* **25**, 97.
55. SCHIN, K. S. and CLEVER, U. (1965). Lysosomal and free acid phos-phatase in salivary glands of developing *Chironomus tentans* larvae. *Science, N.Y.* **150**, 1053.
56. CLEVER, U., STORBECK, I., and ROMBALL, C. G. (1969). Chromosome activity and cell function in polytenic cells. I. Protein synthesis at various stages of larval development. *Expl Cell Res.* **55**, 306.
57. CLEVER, U. (1969). Chromosome activity and cell function in poly-tenic cells. II. The formation of secretion in the salivary glands of *Chironomus*. *Expl Cell Res.* **55**, 317.
58. DOYLE, D. and LAUFER, H. (1969). Requirements of ribonucleic acid synthesis for the formation of salivary gland specific proteins in larval *Chironomus tentans*. *Expl Cell Res.* **57**, 205.
59. GUSTAVSSON, J., FRACCARO, M., TIEPOLO, L., and LINDSTEN, J. (1968). Presumptive X-autosome translocation in a cow: preferential inac-tivation of the normal X chromosome. *Nature, Lond.* **218**, 183.
60. HAMERTON, J. L., GIANNELLI, F., COLLINS, F., HALLETT, J., FRYER, A., MCGUIRE, V. M., and SHORT, R. V. (1969). Non-random X-inac-tivation in the female mule. *Nature, Lond.* **222**, 1277.
61. LYON, M. F., SEARLE, A. G., FORD, C. E., and OHNO, S. (1964). A mouse translocation suppressing sex-linked variegation. *Cytogenetics* **3**, 306.
62. OHNO, S. and LYON, M. F. (1965). Cytological study of Searle's X-autosome translocation in *Mus musculus*. *Chromosoma* **16**, 90.
63. OHNO, S. and CATTANACH, B. M. (1962). Cytological study of an X-autosome translocation in *Mus musculus*. *Cytogenetics* **1**, 129.
64. CATTANACH, B. M. and ISAACSON, J. H. (1967). Controlling elements in the mouse X chromosome. *Genetics, Princeton* **57**, 331.
65. MITTWOCH, U., LELE, K. P., and WEBSTER, W. S. (1965). Relation-ship of Barr bodies, nuclear size and deoxyribonucleic acid value in cultured human cells. *Nature, Lond.* **205**, 477.
66. MITTWOCH, U. (1968). Nuclear sizes in a human diploid/triploid cell culture. *Nature, Lond.* **219**, 1074.
67. KROEGER, H. (1967). Hormones, ion balances and gene activity in

dipteran chromosomes. *Endocrine genetics*, Proc. Symp., Cambridge, 1966 (Ed. S. G. SPICKETT). *Mem. Soc. Endocr.* **15,** 55.

68. KROEGER, H. and LEZZI, M. (1966). Regulation of gene action in insect development. *A. Rev. Ent.* **11,** 1.

69. LEZZI, M. (1966). Induktion eines Ecdyson-aktivierbaren Puff in isolierten Zellkernen von *Chironomus* durch KCl. *Expl Cell Res.* **43,** 571.

70. KROEGER, H. (1963). Experiments on the extranuclear control of gene activity in dipteran polytene chromosomes. *J. cell. comp. Physiol.* **62,** Suppl. I, 45.

71. KROEGER, H. (1964). Zellphysiologische Mechanismen bei der Regulation von Genaktivitäten in den Riesenchromosomen von *Chironomus thummi*. *Chromosoma* **15,** 36.

72. KROEGER, H. (1966). Potentialdifferenz und Puff-muster. Elektrophysiologische und cytologische Untersuchungen an den Speicheldrüsen von *Chironomus thummi*. *Expl. Cell Res.* **41,** 64.

73. LEZZI, M. and KROEGER, H. (1966). Aufnahme von ^{22}Na in die Zellkerne der Speicheldrüsen von *Chironomus thummi*. *Z. Naturf.* **21b,** 274.

74. LEZZI, M. and GILBERT, L. I. (1970). Differential effects of K$^+$ and Na$^+$ on specific bands of isolated polytene chromosomes of *Chironomus tentans*. *J. Cell Sci.* **6,** 615.

75. LOEWENSTEIN, W. R. (1962). Some electrical properties of the membrane of a cell nucleus. *Nature, Lond.* **195,** 462.

76. LOEWENSTEIN, W. R. and KANNO, Y. (1963). Some electrical properties of a nuclear membrane examined with a microelectrode. *J. gen. Physiol.* **46,** 1123.

77. SIEBERT, G., LANGENDORF, H., HANNOVER, R., NITZ-LITZOW, D., PRESSMAN, B. C., and MOORE, C. (1965). Untersuchungen zur Rolle des Natrium-Stoffwechsels im Zellkern der Rattenleber. *Hoppe-Seyler's Z. physiol. Chem.* **343,** 101.

78. SIEBERT, G. (1966). Gewinnung und Funktion isolierter Zellkerne. *Z. klin. Chem.* **3,** 13.

79. RINGERTZ, N. R. and BOLUND, L. (1969). 'Activation' of hen erythrocyte deoxyribonucleoprotein. *Expl Cell Res.* **55,** 205.

80. BLADEN, H. A., BYRNE, R., LEVIN, J. G., and NIRENBERG, M. W. (1965). An electron microscopic study of a DNA-ribosome complex formed *in vitro*. *J. molec. Biol.* **11,** 78.

81. JONES, O. W., DIECKMANN, M., and BERG, P. (1968). Ribosome-induced dissociation of RNA from an RNA polymerase DNA-RNA complex. *J. molec. Biol.* **31,** 177.

82. CRAWLEY, J. C. W. and HARRIS, H. (1963). The fine structure of isolated HeLa cell nuclei. *Expl Cell Res.* **31,** 70.

83. HOLTZMAN, E., SMITH, I., and PENMAN, S. (1966). Electron microscopic studies of detergent-treated HeLa cell nuclei. *J. molec. Biol.* **17,** 131.

84. ROGERS, M. E. (1968). Ribonucleoprotein particles in the amphibian oocyte nucleus. Possible intermediates in ribosome synthesis. *J. Cell Biol.* **36,** 421.

85. MONNERON, A. and MOULÉ, Y. (1968). Etude ultrastructurale de

particules ribonucléoproteiques nucléaires isolées à partir du foie de rat. *Expl Cell Res.* **51,** 531.

86. BERNHARD, W. (1966). Ultrastructural aspects of the normal and pathological nucleolus in mammalian cells. *Natn. Cancer Inst. Monogr.* No. 23, p. 13.

87. McLEISH, J. (1963). Quantitative relationships between deoxyribonucleic and ribonucleic acid in isolated plant nuclei. *Proc. R. Soc.* B **158,** 261.

88. HARRIS, H. (1965). The short-lived RNA in the cell nucleus and its possible role in evolution. *Evolving genes and proteins* (Eds. V. BRYSON and H. J. VOGEL), p. 469. Academic Press, New York.

89. BRUNS, G. P., FISCHER, S., and LOWY, B. A. (1965). A study of the synthesis and interrelationships of ribonucleic acids in duck erythrocytes. *Biochim. biophys. Acta* **95,** 280.

90. ATTARDI, G., PARNAS, H., HWANG, M., and ATTARDI, B. (1966). Giant-size rapidly labeled nuclear RNA and cytoplasmic messenger RNA in immature chick erythrocytes. *J. molec. Biol.* **20,** 145.

91. HOUSSAIS, J.-F. and ATTARDI, G. (1966). High molecular weight non-ribosomal-type nuclear RNA and cytoplasmic messenger RNA in HeLa cells. *Proc. natn. Acad. Sci. U.S.A.* **56,** 616.

92. ADAMS, D. H. (1966). The relationship between cellular nucleic acids in the developing rat cerebral cortex. *Biochem. J.* **98,** 636.

93. OWEN, M. (1967). Uptake of [^{3}H] uridine into precursor pools and RNA in osteogenic cells. *J. Cell Sci.* **2,** 39.

94. LAZARUS, H. M. and SPORN, M. B. (1967). Purification and properties of a nuclear exoribonuclease from Ehrlich ascites tumour cells. *Proc. natn. Acad. Sci. U.S.A.* **57,** 1386.

95. SCHÜTZ, G., GALLWITZ, D., and SEKERIS, C. E. (1968). Rapidly labelled high molecular RNA from rat liver. *Eur. J. Biochem.* **4,** 149.

96. KIJIMA, S. and WILT, F. H. (1969). Rate of nuclear ribonucleic acid turnover in sea urchin embryos. *J. molec. Biol.* **40,** 235.

97. HOGNESS, D. S., COHN, M., and MONOD, J. (1955). Studies on the induced synthesis of β-galactosidase: the kinetics and mechanism of sulphur incorporation. *Biochim. biophys. Acta* **16,** 99.

98. ROTMAN, B. and SPIEGELMAN, S. (1954). On the origin of the carbon in the induced synthesis of β-galactosidase in *Escherichia coli. J. Bact.* **68,** 419.

99. KOCH, A. L. and LEVY, H. R. (1955). Protein turnover in growing cultures of *Escherichia coli. J. biol. Chem.* **217,** 947.

100. HARRIS, H. and WATTS, J. W. (1958). Turnover of protein in a non-multiplying animal cell. *Nature, Lond.* **181,** 1582.

101. MANDELSTAM, J. (1958). Turnover of protein in growing and non-growing populations of *Escherichia coli. Biochem. J.* **69,** 110.

102. EAGLE, H., PIEZ, K. A., FLEISCHMAN, R., and OYAMA, V. I. (1959). Protein turnover in mammalian cell cultures. *J. biol. Chem.* **234,** 592.

103. MANDELSTAM, J. (1960). The intracellular turnover of protein and nucleic acids and its role in biochemical differentiation. *Bact. Rev.* **24,** 289.

104. SCHIMKE, R. T. (1964). The importance of both synthesis and degradation in the control of arginase levels in rat liver. *J. biol. Chem.* **239,** 3808.

105. SCHIMKE, R. T., SWEENEY, E. W., and BERLIN, C. M. (1964). An analysis of the kinetics of rat liver tryptophan pyrrolase induction: the significance of both enzyme synthesis and degradation. *Biochem. biophys. Res. Commun.* **15,** 214.

106. BISHOP, J. O. (1969). The effect of genetic complexity on the time-course of RNA-DNA hybridization. *Biochem. J.* **113,** 805.

107. MELLI, M. and BISHOP, J. D. (1969). Hybridization between rat liver DNA and complementary RNA. *J. molec. Biol.* **40,** 117.

108. BISHOP, J. O., ROBERTSON, F. W., BURNS, J. A., and MELLI, M. (1969). Methods for the analysis of deoxyribonucleic acid-ribonucleic acid hybridization data. *Biochem. J.* **115,** 361.

109. BISHOP, J. O. (1970). Examination of an equilibrium interpretation of deoxyribonucleic acid-ribonucleic acid hybridization data. *Biochem. J.* **116,** 223.

5. Cell fusion

1. The formation of interspecific hybrid cells

THE work that I propose to review in this chapter bears on three of the central problems with which I have been concerned: (1) the nature and specificity of the cytoplasmic signals that regulate RNA synthesis in somatic cell nuclei; (2) the mechanism by which suppression of nuclear RNA synthesis is achieved; (3) the mechanism by which genetic information is transferred from the nucleus to the cytoplasm. This work began in 1965 with an experiment that I made in collaboration with J. F. Watkins.[1] We showed that an animal virus, killed by irradiation with ultraviolet light, could be used to fuse together cells derived from mouse and man to produce artificial man-mouse hybrid cells. The idea of using viruses in this way has its origins in observations that go back for more than a century.[2] Many diseases have long been known to be associated with lesions in which multinucleate cells are found. In the medical literature of the nineteenth century there is a protracted and vigorous controversy about the mode of formation of these cells. Multinucleate cells are commonly found in the lesions produced by certain pathogenic viruses and, during the last decade, it has become clear that in at least some cases the virus produces the multinucleate cell by fusing single cells together. It was thus a very small step to attempt to see whether a virus could be used to fuse together cells of different kinds, and whether the resulting hybrid cells, if they were formed, would survive. And since the survival of the hybrid cells might be jeopardized by infection with a living virus, the virus was killed before the cells were treated with it. In the event, it turned out that viruses, inactivated by ultraviolet light, could be used to provide a general method for fusing together both differentiated and un-differentiated cells from different species and even different orders of vertebrates.[3,4] The resulting interspecific hybrid cells survived for long periods and, in many cases, proved capable of indefinite multiplication.[5,6] They thus offered interesting possibilities for the study of nucleo-cytoplasmic relationships and lent themselves to experiments of a kind that had not hitherto been feasible. Some of these experiments I now propose to discuss.

The virus used in this work was the 'Sendai' virus, a member of the para-influenza group of myxoviruses. Sendai virus was chosen because it had been shown by Okada[7] that animal tumour cells in suspension could be rapidly fused together by high concentrations of this virus. The virus was irradiated with doses of ultraviolet light that reduced its infectivity by at least 10^6; but the dead virus retained its ability to fuse cells together. The two cell types studied in the first instance were the HeLa cell (a cell of human origin that has been grown for many years in artificial culture) and the Ehrlich ascites cell (a tumour that grows as a cell suspension in the peritoneal cavity of the mouse). These two cell types were chosen for a number of technical reasons, but mainly because their nuclei were easily distinguishable on morphological grounds. When a suspension containing a mixture of the two cell types is treated with the dead virus under appropriate conditions the cells clump together, and electron micrographs of these clumps show the virus particles trapped among the interdigitations of the microvilli on the surfaces of the cells.[8] When the virus-treated cells are incubated at 37°C the cell surfaces at points of contact between the cells fuse together so that small cytoplasmic bridges are formed (Plate 4). These bridges increase in number and in extent until eventually the cytoplasms of neighbouring cells coalesce, so that multinucleate cells containing varying numbers of nuclei are formed (Plate 5a).

When these multinucleate cells are introduced into a culture chamber they adhere to the glass floor of the chamber, or to coverslips introduced into it, and within 3 or 4 h spread out over the surface of the glass. Stained preparations then reveal that many of the cells contain two sorts of nuclei, one having the characteristics of HeLa nuclei, the other those of Ehrlich nuclei. In order to confirm that these multinucleate cells were indeed heterokaryons (that is to say, that they contained nuclei of different kinds), a population of HeLa cells was grown in the presence of tritiated thymidine until virtually all the cell nuclei were labelled; and a suspension containing these labelled HeLa cells and unlabelled Ehrlich cells was treated with the virus. The resulting multinucleate cells were then allowed to spread out over glass coverslips and autoradiographs were made of fixed and suitably extracted preparations. These autoradiographs showed that the multinucleate cells contained both labelled and unlabelled nuclei; the labelled nuclei clearly resembled HeLa nuclei and the unlabelled nuclei clearly resembled Ehrlich nuclei (Plate 5*b*). There was thus no doubt that hybrid cells containing both human and murine nuclei had been formed under the influence of the virus.

2. *Synthesis of macromolecules in hybrid cells*

It was then of interest to see what these hybrid cells were capable of doing. Would they synthesize protein, RNA, and DNA, and would they undergo mitosis? Exposure of the hybrid cells to tritiated leucine reveals that they do synthesize protein, and the labelling seen in autoradiographs of such cells is not obviously different in distribution or intensity from that seen in neighbouring mononucleate cells. When the hybrid cells are exposed for a few minutes to a tritiated precursor of RNA, autoradiographs show that in the heterokaryon both sets of nuclei are labelled. It is therefore clear that in these hybrid cells the genes of both mouse and man are transcribed. More prolonged incubation with radioactive RNA precursors results in labelling of the cytoplasmic RNA. The pattern of RNA synthesis in the heterokaryon is thus no different from that seen in normal animal cells except that both the human and the murine nuclei contribute to the process. Labelling with tritiated thymidine shows that both sets of nuclei also synthesize DNA. Initially, synthesis of DNA does not occur synchronously in all the nuclei of a multinucleate cell, but an increasing measure of synchrony is progressively imposed. Synchronization of DNA synthesis is readily achieved in multinucleate cells containing nuclei of the same type and also in some heterokaryons containing nuclei of different types; but, in certain cases, fusion of cells of widely different origin may be associated with persistent asynchrony of DNA synthesis in the heterokaryon. Synchronization of DNA synthesis is usually more complete in cells containing only two nuclei than in those containing higher numbers.[9-11]

3. Formation and behaviour of mononucleate hybrid cells

Although multinucleate cells produced by cell fusion may, under favourable conditions, remain alive for several weeks, their continued reproduction is conditional upon the formation of daughter cells that contain a single nucleus. This process may be achieved in a variety of ways, but all of them are mediated by the fusion of the individual nuclei in the multinucleate cell into larger units. This fusion takes place at mitosis. In binucleate cells, synchronous mitosis of the two nuclei is commonly associated with the formation of a single spindle. All the chromosomes become aligned along a single metaphase plate, and division of the cell produces two mononucleate daughters that contain within one nucleus the chromosomes of both parent cells (Plate 6). Other forms of mitosis are also seen, especially tripolar and tetrapolar mitosis, which give rise to variable numbers of daughter cells, some of which may be binucleate. In other cases, the nuclei in the heterokaryon may enter mitosis, but cell division may not occur. Post-mitotic reconstitution may then gather all the chromosomes of the cell into a single very large nucleus, or two nuclei may be formed, each containing both the parental sets of chromosomes. Where heterokaryons contain more than two nuclei irregular and abortive mitosis becomes increasingly common, but daughter cells containing more than two parental chromosomal sets are sometimes produced. There are thus several ways in which a heterokaryon can generate daughter cells in which a single nucleus contains genetic components from both parents.

These hybrid mononucleate daughter cells also synthesize protein, RNA, and DNA and may in turn undergo mitosis. At metaphase they show, in varying proportions, the chromosomal complements of the two parent cells (Plate 7a). Many of these mononucleate daughter cells are capable of indefinite multiplication, and, over a wide range, species differences in the parent cells do not appear to affect the ability of the daughter cells to multiply. Mononucleate hybrid cells capable of indefinite multiplication have now been produced by virus-induced fusion between cells derived from mouse and hamster,[12] mouse and man,[13, 14] and even mouse and chick.[15] These experiments show that cells from widely different species of vertebrate may be perfectly compatible with each other when they are amalgamated into a single unit. It thus appears that in the cells of vertebrates there are, in general, no *intracellular* mechanisms for the recognition of incompatibility similar to those responsible for the recognition and destruction of tissue or organ grafts exchanged between different individuals. Not only do the cytoplasms of these different cells fuse amicably together, but their nuclei also; and after nuclear fusion has taken place the composite cell carries out its functions in a completely integrated way.

4. Hybrids made from differentiated cells

Hybrid cells of the type I have been describing are formed by the fusion of two cells each of which is normally capable of RNA synthesis, DNA synthesis, and multiplication; but heterokaryons can also be made with cells in which the synthesis of RNA or DNA or both is partially or wholly suppressed. Cells that show restrictions in their ability to synthesize one or other nucleic acid may be fused with each other or with cells that show no such restrictions. These specialized types of heterokaryon have been particularly useful in the analysis of the cytoplasmic stimuli that regulate RNA synthesis in animal cell nuclei and the mechanisms by which this regulation is brought about. Three highly differentiated animal cells were chosen for special study. These were the rabbit macrophage, the rat lymphocyte, and the hen erythrocyte. Macrophages are motile, phagocytic cells, whose main function is the removal of debris from the tissues of the body. These cells can be obtained in large numbers from the peritoneal cavity of the rabbit after certain experimental procedures. They commonly have an oval or kidney-shaped nucleus. The macrophages that one obtains from the peritoneal cavity of the rabbit all synthesize RNA, but they do not, either in the peritoneal cavity or *in vitro*, synthesize DNA or undergo mitosis.[16] The lymphocyte is a small cell with a dense compact nucleus and very little cytoplasm. In the rat,

PLATE 13

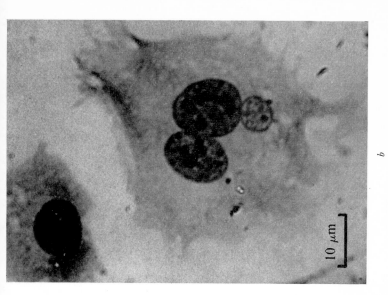

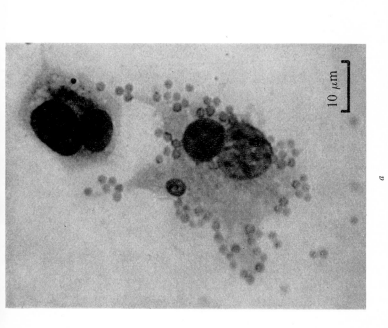

a

a. A heterokaryon containing two mouse nuclei and one hen erythrocyte nucleus, 18 h after cell fusion. The haemadsorption reaction reveals the presence of hen-specific antigens on the surface of the cell.

b. A heterokaryon containing two mouse nuclei and one hen erythrocyte nucleus, 5 days after cell fusion. The erythrocyte nucleus has been reactivated, but the absence of any haemadsorption shows that the hen-specific antigens are no longer present on the surface of the cell. The erythrocyte nucleus shows a small nucleolus.

PLATE 14

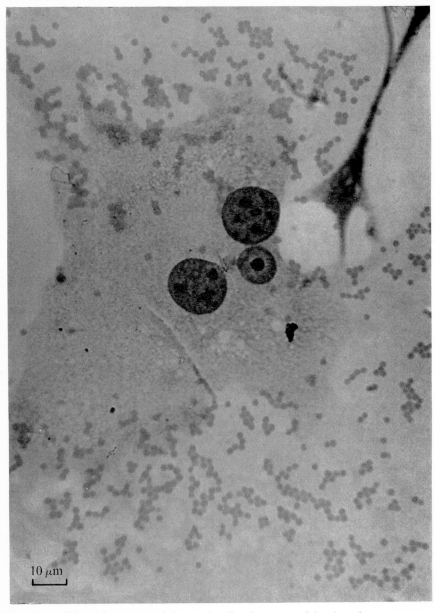

A heterokaryon containing two irradiated mouse nuclei and one hen erythrocyte nucleus, 11 days after cell fusion. This is now a typical radiation giant cell. The reactivated erythrocyte nucleus has a prominent nucleolus, and hen-specific antigens have reappeared on the surface of the cell.

PLATE 15

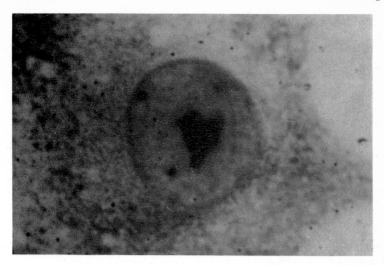

a. Autoradiograph of an A_9 cell exposed for 4 h to tritiated hypoxanthine. There is very little incorporation of the label. Under such conditions a normal mouse cell would be very heavily labelled.

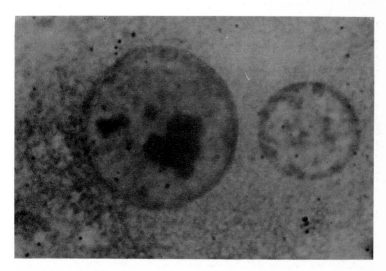

b. Autoradiograph of an A_9–chick erythrocyte in which the erythrocyte nucleus has been reactivated but has not yet developed a nucleolus. The cell has been exposed for 4 h to tritiated hypoxanthine, but there is still very little incorporation of label.

PLATE 16

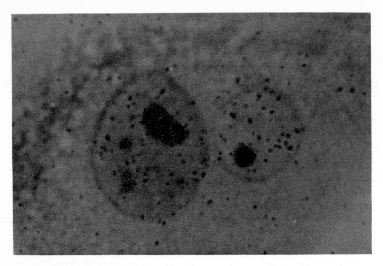

a. Autoradiograph of an A_9–chick erythrocyte heterokaryon in which the erythrocyte nucleus shows early development of the nucleolus. The cell has been exposed for 4 h to tritiated hypoxanthine. Both the A_9 and the erythrocyte nucleus are now clearly labelled. The cell has acquired the ability to incorporate hypoxanthine into nucleic acid.

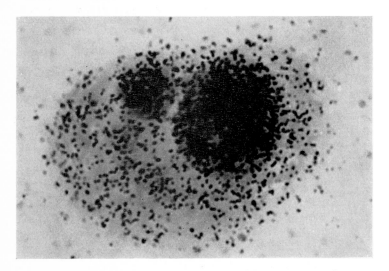

b. Autoradiograph of a heterokaryon containing a mouse nucleus and a chick erythrocyte nucleus, exposed for 6 h to a tritiated RNA precursor. Both the mouse nucleus and the erythrocyte are very heavily labelled, and there is also substantial cytoplasmic labelling.

PLATE 17

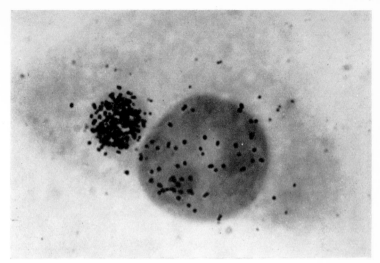

a. Autoradiograph of another heterokaryon from the same preparation as the cell shown in pl. 16*b*. The mouse nucleus has been inactivated by ultraviolet light. The erythrocyte nucleus, which has not yet developed a nucleolus, is heavily labelled, but the cytoplasm contains very little radioactivity.

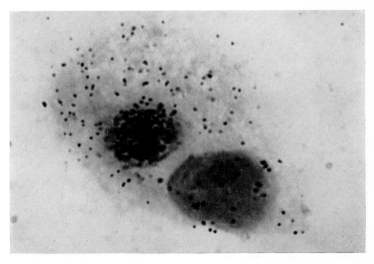

b. Autoradiograph of a heterokaryon treated in the same way as the cell shown in pl. 17*a*, but after the erythrocyte nucleus had developed a nucleolus. The cytoplasm of the cell is now labelled.

PLATE 18

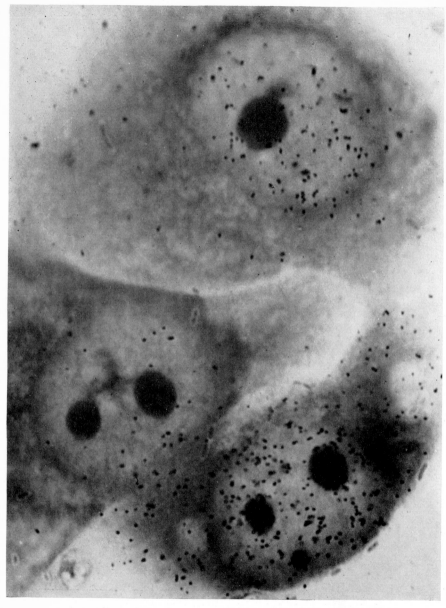

Autoradiograph showing a normal HeLa cell (top left), a HeLa cell in which the whole nucleus has been irradiated with ultraviolet light (top right), and a HeLa cell in which the nucleolus only has been irradiated (bottom). The preparation was exposed to a radioactive RNA precursor for 6 h. Irradiation of the nucleolus alone, despite continued synthesis of RNA elsewhere in the nucleus, reduces cytoplasmic labelling to a level comparable with that seen in the cell in which the whole nucleus has been irradiated.

almost pure populations of lymphocytes can be obtained by
cannulation of the thoracic duct. These small lymphocytes
synthesize variable amounts of RNA: when exposed for an
hour to high concentrations of a radioactive RNA precursor
some of the cells synthesize so little RNA that the amount of
radioactivity incorporated is barely detectable, while other
cells incorporate easily measurable amounts of radioactivity
under the same conditions.[17] Small lymphocytes do not normally synthesize DNA or undergo mitosis; but they can be induced to resume the synthesis of DNA and to undergo mitosis
when they are exposed to certain antigenic stimuli.[18] The small
lymphocyte then becomes transformed into a cell that plays a
crucial role in the immune responses of the body. Whereas
mammalian erythrocytes normally eliminate their nuclei during
the process of maturation, the red blood cells of birds, amphibians, reptiles, and certain other orders of vertebrate retain
their nuclei throughout the life cycle of the cell. In the hen,
these nucleated erythrocytes, when mature, do not synthesize
measurable amounts of RNA,[19] nor do they synthesize DNA or
undergo mitosis. They are thus 'end-cells': after a variable
period of circulation in the blood they are removed and
destroyed. It was of interest in the first instance to determine,
especially in the case of the nucleated erythrocyte, to what extent these changes produced by differentiation were reversible.
Could the inert or partially inactive cell be induced to resume
the synthesis of RNA or DNA or both, if it was incorporated in
a heterokaryon together with a cell that synthesized both RNA
and DNA in the normal way?

By varying the ratio of the two cell types used and the concentration of inactivated virus, the average number of nuclei
per heterokaryon and the proportion of each kind of nucleus
can, over a certain range, be controlled. Plate 7*b* shows a
heterokaryon produced by fusing one HeLa cell with nine
rabbit macrophages; and Plate 8*a* shows a heterokaryon produced by fusing three HeLa cells with two rat lymphocytes.
When HeLa-rabbit macrophage heterokaryons are exposed for
short periods to tritiated RNA precursors, suitably fixed and
extracted autoradiographs reveal that both sets of nuclei in the
heterokaryon synthesize RNA; and more prolonged exposure
to these precursors results, as usual, in labelling of cytoplasmic

RNA. It is thus clear that in these heterokaryons, as in the HeLa-Ehrlich heterokaryons, both sets of nuclei contribute to the synthesis of the cell's RNA. Since both the HeLa cell and the macrophage normally synthesize RNA, this result is not unexpected. Of greater interest, however, is the fact that when these heterokaryons are exposed to tritiated thymidine, the macrophage nuclei as well as the HeLa nuclei become labelled. Twenty-four hours after cell fusion, an hour's exposure to tritiated thymidine may label as many as 80 per cent of the macrophage nuclei in the heterokaryons. It is therefore clear that the inability of the macrophage to synthesize DNA, and hence replicate its genetic material, is reversible: DNA synthesis is resumed in the macrophage nucleus when the macrophage is fused with a HeLa cell.

An essentially similar result is obtained with HeLa-rat lymphocyte heterokaryons. A 20-min exposure of these cells to tritiated uridine labels virtually all the HeLa and all the lymphocyte nuclei in them. Since about half of the small lymphocytes in the thoracic duct are not labelled by even an hour's exposure to high concentrations of radioactive RNA precursors, it is probable that many of the lymphocyte nuclei in the heterokaryons have been induced to resume, or at least greatly increase, the synthesis of RNA. And when HeLa-lymphocyte heterokaryons are exposed to tritiated thymidine, not only the HeLa nuclei but also the lymphocyte nuclei are found to be synthesizing DNA. The results obtained with HeLa-hen erythrocyte heterokaryons (Plate 8*b*) are even more striking. Mature hen erythrocytes do not incorporate radioactive precursors into RNA or DNA in amounts detectable by autoradiography. Even when the cells are incubated with high concentrations of tritiated ribonucleosides or tritiated thymidine for several hours, autoradiographs extracted in the appropriate way show no significant labelling of the cell nuclei. However, when HeLa-hen erythrocyte heterokaryons are exposed to tritiated uridine for as little as 15–20 min, not only the HeLa nuclei, but also the majority of the erythrocyte nuclei are found to be synthesizing RNA. It can therefore be concluded that in these heterokaryons the erythrocyte nuclei, which are normally inert, have been induced to resume genetic activity. Labelling with tritiated thymidine reveals that many of the hen erythrocyte nuclei in the heterokaryons have also been induced to resume the synthesis of DNA.[10] Since, among nucleated cells, bird erythrocytes represent perhaps the most extreme form of differentiation seen in vertebrates, one is probably justified in concluding that, so long as the cell retains its nucleus, all restrictions on nucleic acid synthesis imposed by the process of differentiation are reversible.

It might, however, be supposed that these dormant or partially inactive nuclei resume the synthesis of RNA and DNA in the heterokaryon not because they now find themselves in the cytoplasm of a cell that instructs its nuclei to synthesize RNA and DNA, but because they find themselves in *foreign* cytoplasm: the resumption of activity might be regarded as a non-specific reaction to 'foreignness'. This idea can be tested in a number of ways, one of which is to study the behaviour of heterokaryons made by fusing these differentiated cells with each other. Thus, for example, heterokaryons may be formed by fusing together rabbit macrophages and rat lymphocytes or rabbit macrophages and hen erythrocytes. The nuclei are then in foreign or partially foreign cytoplasm; but the heterokaryons differ from those made with HeLa cells in that neither of the parent cells normally synthesizes DNA. Such heterokaryons might therefore be expected to reveal whether the resumption of DNA synthesis in the dormant nucleus is determined simply by foreignness of the cytoplasm in the heterokaryon, or whether other factors are involved.

Plate 9*a* shows a heterokaryon containing three rabbit macrophage nuclei and two rat lymphocyte nuclei; and Plate 9*b* shows a heterokaryon containing four rabbit macrophage nuclei and three hen erythrocyte nuclei. It will be seen that the nuclei in these cases are distributed as a rosette at the periphery of the cells. This peripheral distribution of nuclei in certain types of multinucleate cell was first discussed by Langhans,[20] and when such cells are found in pathological conditions they are commonly referred to as 'Langhans' giant cells. This peculiar morphology appears to be characteristic of multinucleate cells in which the macrophage is the dominant cell type. When macrophage-lymphocyte heterokaryons are exposed to tritiated uridine, both sets of nuclei are found to be synthesizing RNA, thus showing that in these cells both sets of

genes are again active. Both sets of nuclei in macrophage-
erythrocyte heterokaryons also synthesize RNA, which indicates that rabbit macrophage cytoplasm, as well as HeLa
cytoplasm, will induce the dormant hen erythrocyte nuclei to
resume genetic activity. But none of these heterokaryons synthesizes DNA or undergoes mitosis: they may be exposed to
tritiated thymidine at any time after cell fusion, but none of
their nuclei becomes labelled. On the other hand, if chick
embryo fibroblasts are fused with erythrocytes from the same
embryo, the erythrocyte nuclei in the heterokaryons resume the
synthesis of DNA even though they are not now in foreign
cytoplasm. It is therefore clear that these dormant nuclei resume
the synthesis of DNA in heterokaryons not because they are
introduced into foreign cytoplasm, but because they are introduced into cytoplasm that instructs its nuclei to synthesize
DNA; and when an erythrocyte nucleus is introduced into the
cytoplasm of a macrophage, which normally synthesize RNA
but not DNA, then the erythrocyte nucleus is induced to
synthesize RNA but not DNA.

The results of these experiments with differentiated cells are
summarized in Table 1, from which it will be seen that certain

TABLE I

Synthesis of RNA *and* DNA *in heterokaryons*

	RNA	DNA
Cell type		
HeLa	+	+
rabbit macrophage	+	o
rat lymphocyte	+	o
hen erythrocyte	o	o
Cell combination in heterokaryon		
HeLa–HeLa	+ +	+ +
HeLa–rabbit macrophage	+ +	+ +
HeLa–rat lymphocyte	+ +	+ +
HeLa–hen erythrocyte	+ +	+ +
rabbit macrophage–rabbit macrophage	+ +	oo
rabbit macrophage–rat lymphocyte	+ +	oo
rabbit macrophage–hen erythrocyte	+ +	oo

o, No synthesis in any nuclei; oo, no synthesis in any nuclei of either
type; +, synthesis in some or all nuclei; + +, synthesis in some or all
nuclei of both types.

general principles emerge. (1) If either of the parent cells normally synthesizes RNA, then RNA synthesis will take place in both types of nuclei in the heterokaryon. (2) If either of the parent cells normally synthesizes DNA, then DNA synthesis will take place in both types of nuclei in the heterokaryon. (3) If neither of the parent cells normally synthesizes DNA, then no synthesis of DNA takes place in the heterokaryon. The regulation of nucleic acid synthesis in the heterokaryon is thus essentially unilateral: whenever a cell that synthesizes a particular nucleic acid is fused with one that does not, the active cell initiates this synthesis in the inactive partner. In no case does the inactive cell suppress synthesis in the active partner, even in those heterokaryons, like the HeLa-macrophage heterokaryon shown in Plate 7b, in which a number of inactive cells are fused with one active cell. In the terminology currently used to describe similar effects in bacteria, the synthesis of RNA and DNA in this situation may be said to be under 'positive control'.

5. The nature of the cytoplasmic signals

In considering the nature of the cytoplasmic signals that 'turn on' nucleic acid synthesis in these inactive or partially inactive nuclei, the heterokaryons containing hen erythrocyte nuclei are of special importance. All the other heterokaryons that I have described are produced by the simple fusion of the two parent cells and thus contain the nuclei and the cytoplasms of both parents. This is not, in general, the case for heterokaryons in which one of the parents is a nucleated erythrocyte. Sendai virus is a haemolytic virus, and at the high concentrations used to promote cell fusion it induces haemolysis of the red cells, so that their cytoplasmic contents are lost. The haemolysed red cells, which consist of little more than a cell nucleus and a leaky cell membrane, are referred to as erythrocyte ghosts. When mixed suspensions of hen erythrocytes and human or mouse tissue culture cells are treated with the virus, electron micrographs show the erythrocyte ghosts and the other cells stuck together in mixed clumps; and virus particles may be seen between the adjacent cell surfaces (Plate 10a). Under the influence of the virus, bridges are formed in the usual way between the membrane of the tissue culture cell and that of the erythrocyte ghost, and through these bridges the cytoplasm of the human or mouse cell flows to fill the space vacated by the cytoplasmic contents of the red cell itself (Plate 10*b*). Progressive dissolution of the contiguous regions of the apposed cell membranes eventually permits the red cell nucleus to be incorporated completely into the cytoplasm of the other cell (Plate 11*a*, *b*). In this case, therefore, the heterokaryon is formed essentially by transplantation of the erythrocyte nucleus, divested of its own cytoplasm, into the cytoplasm of the human or mouse cell.

The very fact that interspecific hybrid cells may function in a perfectly integrated way at once tells us something of importance about the mechanisms that regulate gene activity. We can be confident that the signals that the hybrid cytoplasm transmits to the genes of one of the species in the hybrid cell do not represent false signals to the genes of the other species. If such false signals were given, the end result would be a progressive disorganization of cell metabolism. But we know that some interspecific hybrid cells actually multiply more vigorously than either of their parent cells; so we can dismiss the idea that the signals emanating from the hybrid cytoplasm are misunderstood by either set of genes. And this must mean either that each set of genes reacts only to signals from its own cytoplasmic components, or that the signals that the hybrid cytoplasm transmits to the genes produce the same effect on both sets of genes. The demonstration that erythrocyte nuclei can be introduced into other cells without any appreciable contribution of erythrocyte cytoplasm permits us to decide which of these two alternatives is correct. The experiments I have already described make it clear that reactivation of the hen erythrocyte nucleus does not require the activity of hen cytoplasm. Erythrocyte nuclei, freed of their own cytoplasm by the haemolytic action of the Sendai virus, can be reactivated in the cytoplasm of cells from a wide variety of animal species, ranging from mouse to man; and frog erythrocyte nuclei can also be reactivated in these cells.[2] It is thus obvious that these nuclei *do* respond to signals emanating from grossly foreign cytoplasm. The remarkable integration of interspecific hybrid cells cannot therefore be due to the fact that each set of genes responds only to signals from its own cytoplasmic components. The reactivation of hen erythrocyte nuclei in human or mouse cytoplasm involves not only the resumption of nucleic acid synthesis, but also, as I shall show later, the ordered synthesis of specific proteins determined by these nuclei. We can therefore conclude that the signals emanating from human or mouse cytoplasm are understood perfectly well by hen nuclei. In short, these cytoplasmic signals are not species-specific.

The outstanding morphological event associated with the reactivation of the erythrocyte nucleus is a massive increase in volume.[21] While accurate measurements of nuclear volume are difficult, it is likely that there is at least a twentyfold to thirty-fold increase.[22] This expansion of the nucleus is accompanied by dispersion of its highly condensed chromatin, a process that is easily demonstrated with appropriate cytological stains (Plates 11b and 12a). If these heterokaryons are exposed for a few minutes to a radioactive RNA precursor, it can be shown by autoradiographic methods that the amount of RNA synthesized per unit time in the reactivated erythrocyte nucleus is directly related to the degree of enlargement which it has undergone (Plate 12b). As shown in Fig. 7, the amount of RNA synthesized by the erythrocyte nucleus is a simple function of its volume; and those erythrocyte nuclei that have not undergone enlargement do not synthesize RNA. The increase in volume of the nucleus is not simply due to the ingress of water; there is at least a fourfold to sixfold increase in dry mass, which is largely accounted for by an increase in protein content.[22] If the erythrocytes are irradiated with a large dose of ultraviolet light before the heterokaryons are made, synthesis of RNA and DNA in the erythrocyte nuclei is largely suppressed; but the irradiated nuclei none the less undergo enlargement in the usual way.[21] This means that the increase in volume that the erythrocyte nuclei undergo on reactivation is not the consequence of the increased synthesis and accumulation of RNA and DNA; enlargement is the cardinal event and the progressive increase in the synthesis of nucleic acid is governed by it. When they enlarge in the heterokaryon, erythrocyte nuclei in which RNA synthesis has been suppressed by ultraviolet irradiation show the same increase in dry mass as unirradiated nuclei.[23] The irradiated nuclei cannot be synthesizing their own proteins under these conditions, so that the increase in dry mass that the erythrocyte nuclei undergo on reactivation must be due very largely to a flow of proteins from the cytoplasm into these nuclei. These proteins are, of course, human or mouse proteins, as the case may be, but they are none the less able to do whatever they need to do in the hen nucleus. Until the hen

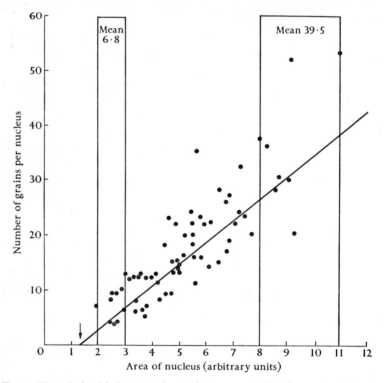

Fig. 7. The relationship between the maximum cross-sectional area of erythrocyte nuclei (a measure of their volume) in heterokaryons and the number of grains overlying these nuclei in autoradiographs. The cells were exposed for 20 min to [³H] uridine. The arrow indicates the mean cross-sectional area of unenlarged erythrocyte nuclei. (From Harris.[21])

nucleus determines the synthesis of hen proteins in the hetero-karyon, we must regard it as operating, and operating perfectly well, in an environment composed for the most part of foreign proteins.

The dispersion of the chromatin that takes place as the erythrocyte nuclei enlarge is associated with certain structural changes that can be measured by cytochemical techniques. Of these changes, the most striking is a markedly increased affinity of the chromatin for intercalating dyes such as acridine orange and ethidium bromide.[22] Even before replication of DNA begins, there is at least a fourfold increase in the amount of acridine orange that the chromatin can bind, and the amount of dye bound increases still further as nuclear enlargement proceeds. When the ability of the chromatin to bind actinomycin D is measured by an assay that defines the specific 'tight' binding between the antibiotic and the DNA, a similar increase is observed as the nucleus enlarges.[24] Reactivation of the chromatin is also accompanied by changes in its melting profile that reveal an increased susceptibility to heat denaturation.[22] All these observations reflect the fact that nuclear enlargement loosens the chromatin and renders it more accessible, not only to macromolecules, but even to smaller molecules such as the acridine dyes and actinomycin. The same process no doubt also renders the chromatin more accessible to the molecules involved in its transcription, so that, as more of the initially condensed chromatin opens up, more of it is transcribed.

Many of the cytochemical changes that the erythrocyte nucleus undergoes when it is reactivated in the heterokaryon can be mimicked in erythrocyte ghosts if these are treated under certain conditions with agents that chelate divalent cations.[22, 25] It therefore seems likely that in these erythrocyte nuclei, as in the nuclei of other eukaryotic cells, the mechanisms that regulate the transcription of the DNA involve, among other things, the interaction of the chromatin with divalent cations and other electrolytes. I have already mentioned in Chapter 4 the association between changes in nuclear volume and the appearance of condensed X chromosomes and accessory chromocentres in the somatic cells of certain vertebrates;[26-28] and I have discussed how changes in the electrolyte environment of the chromatin could produce selective condensation, and hence inactivation, of different genetic regions. The observations that have been made on erythrocyte nuclei reactivated in heterokaryons are entirely consistent with the view that genetic activity is regulated by selective condensation and dispersion of the chromatin; and the relationship that has been established between RNA synthesis and nuclear volume suggests the possibility that changes in the volume of the nucleus may be part of a general mechanism that permits large genetic areas to be opened up or closed down in an ordered way. In any case, if the reactivation of the dormant erythrocyte nuclei is achieved by changes in the electrolyte environment of the chromatin, it is not surprising that this re-activation takes place in cytoplasm from widely different species. On this view, the signals that pass to the hen nuclei from human or mouse cytoplasm would be of a quite general kind likely to be common to all vertebrate cells.

6. Transfer of information from nucleus to cytoplasm: evidence from the behaviour of reactivated erythrocyte nuclei

Heterokaryons in which one of the parent cells is a nucleated erythrocyte present an unparalleled opportunity to examine the whole process by which genetic information is expressed in mammalian cells. The erythrocyte nucleus is initially in a completely repressed state, and its reactivation takes place slowly enough to permit piecemeal dissection of the process. The reactivated nuclei can be re-isolated from the heterokaryon at any time, and the nature of the RNA that they are making can be examined. The passage of RNA from the reactivated nuclei to the cytoplasm of the cell can be monitored; and the relationship between the transcription of genes and the syn-thesis of proteins specified by these genes can be determined. In short, the whole process of information transfer can be analysed in these heterokaryons with a degree of precision that is hardly attainable in any other biological system. In this section, I shall present the results of such an analysis.

In studying the synthesis of any protein that might be deter-mined by the hen erythrocyte nucleus reactivated in human or mouse cytoplasm, the first requirement is to show that the protein being examined is hen, and not human or mouse, protein. It was for this reason that the first proteins chosen for investigation in these heterokaryons were species-specific sur-face antigens.[29] These antigens can be detected on the surface of cells in culture with great sensitivity and complete specificity by the technique of immune haemadsorption,[30, 31] an appli-cation of the mixed antiglobulin reaction.[32] Sensitized red cells serve as the marker, and specific antiserum binds these red cells to surfaces bearing the appropriate antigens, but not to others. There is no cross-reaction, at suitable dilutions of antiserum, between hen surface antigens and human or mouse antigens, so that, in these heterokaryons, adsorbed red cells indicate the presence of hen-specific antigens.

Since the formation of these heterokaryons involves the fusion of the recipient cell with the erythrocyte ghost, membrane components derived from the erythrocyte are present in the surface of the heterokaryon immediately after fusion.[8] Immune haemadsorption reveals the presence of the hen-specific antigens (Plate 13a). The behaviour of these antigens during the first few days after cell fusion presents an interesting paradox. Since the hen erythrocyte nuclei undergo reactivation during this period and synthesize large amounts of RNA, one might have expected that the amount of hen-specific antigen on the surface of the heterokaryon would increase. Instead, it was found that these antigens gradually disappeared from the cell surface and, by the fourth day after fusion, could not be detected at all in the great majority of the cells (Plate 13b). Analysis of this phenomenon revealed that the disappearance of the hen-specific antigens initially present on the surface of the heterokaryons was due to their progressive displacement by human or mouse antigens that continued to be produced by the human or mouse cells into which the erythrocyte nuclei had been introduced. During this period the erythrocyte nuclei, although they synthesized large amounts of RNA, did not determine the appearance of any new hen-specific antigens on the surface of the heterokaryon; nor did they influence the rate of disappearance of the hen-specific antigens introduced by the process of cell fusion.

In one important respect the reactivation of the erythrocyte nuclei during the first two or three days after cell fusion is incomplete. Although these nuclei undergo great enlargement and resume the synthesis of RNA and DNA, they do not develop normal nucleoli (Plate 12b). On the third, and occasionally on the second, day after cell fusion, some erythrocyte nuclei develop small structures, which, under the light microscope, appear to be rudimentary nucleoli; but the prominent nucleoli characteristic of tissue cells in culture are not seen. Since the erythrocytes are taken from normal animals, there is no reason to suspect a genetic defect in this respect. One might therefore suppose either that the human or mouse cytoplasm is, in some unidentified way, an inadequate environment for the hen erythrocyte nucleus, or that these heterokaryons do not survive long enough as multinucleate cells to permit the nucleolus to develop fully in the erythrocyte nucleus. Within four days of cell fusion virtually all the heterokaryons enter mitosis, which, in one way or another, results in the disappearance of the erythrocyte nuclei as separate bodies. In order to permit development of the erythrocyte nuclei within the heterokaryons for a longer period, the recipient cells were therefore subjected to an appropriate dose of gamma radiation. The irradiated cells continued to grow for up to 3 weeks without undergoing mitosis and thus permitted the further development of the erythrocyte nuclei as discrete entities. In these irradiated cells, nucleoli began to appear in the erythrocyte nuclei on the third day after cell fusion and became progressively larger. By the eleventh day, more than 80 per cent of the erythrocyte nuclei contained one or two readily identifiable nucleoli (Plate 14). Hen-specific antigens could be detected on the surface of virtually all these irradiated heterokaryons immediately after cell fusion and for about 24 hours thereafter. These antigens were then progressively eliminated in the usual way and, by the sixth day, no hen-specific antigen could be detected in any of the cultures. On the eighth day, however, traces of hen-specific antigen began to reappear in some of the cells: the antigen was first observed on the tips of elongated cytoplasmic processes. On succeeding days, increasing numbers of cells showed the presence of the antigen, which could now be detected all over the periphery of the cells. The amount of antigen per cell, as judged by the intensity of the haemadsorption reaction, continued to increase until, by the eleventh day, most of the heterokaryons showed strong haemadsorption over the whole of their periphery. The intensity of the haemadsorption greatly exceeded that seen in heterokaryons immediately after cell fusion. This sequence of events is illustrated in Plates 13a, b and 14 and plotted, as a function of time, in Fig. 8.

When the same experiment was done with erythrocytes from 12-day-old chick embryos, essentially similar results were obtained, except that the whole process took place more rapidly. Nucleoli began to appear in the erythrocyte nuclei on the

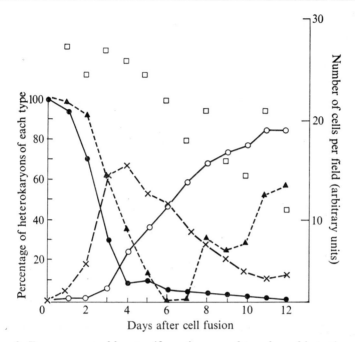

FIG. 8. Reappearance of hen-specific antigens on the surface of heterokaryons made by fusing irradiated mouse cells with adult hen erythrocytes. The relationships between the enlargement of the erythrocyte nucleus, the development of nucleoli within it, and the disappearance and reappearance of the hen-specific surface antigens are shown. □, Total number of cells; ●, heterokaryons with unenlarged erythrocyte nuclei; ×, heterokaryons with enlarged erythrocyte nuclei, but no visible nucleoli; ○, heterokaryons with enlarged erythrocyte nuclei containing visible nucleoli; ▲, heterokaryons showing hen-specific surface antigens.

second day after fusion, and the *de novo* appearance of chick-specific surface antigens took place before the antigens introduced during cell fusion were completely eliminated (Fig. 9). When erythrocytes from even younger chick embryos were used, the appearance of nucleoli and of new surface antigens occurred even sooner. In all cases, there was a clear correlation between the speed with which the nucleoli developed and the time at which the species-specific antigens re-appeared on the surface of the cells. These experiments thus indicated that hen erythrocyte nuclei, operating in the cytoplasm of cells from widely different animal species, where capable of determining the appearance of hen-specific surface antigens in these cells;

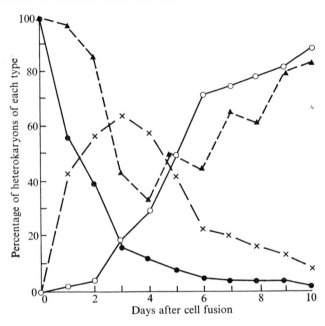

Fig. 9. Reappearance of hen-specific antigens on the surface of heterokaryons made by fusing irradiated mouse cells with chick embryo erythrocytes. The relationships between the enlargement of the erythrocyte nucleus, the development of nucleoli within it, and the disappearance and reappearance of the hen-specific surface antigens are shown. ●, Heterokaryons with enlarged erythrocyte nuclei; x, heterokaryons with enlarged erythrocyte nuclei, but no visible nucleoli; ○, heterokaryons with enlarged erythrocyte nuclei containing visible nucleoli; ▲, heterokaryons showing hen-specific surface antigens.

but the reactivated erythrocyte nuclei did not determine the appearance of these antigens until they developed nucleoli.

Since these species-specific antigens were only detected when they appeared at the surface of the cell, the possibility existed that there might be a lag between the time of their synthesis and the time of their detection by the haemadsorption technique. If this lag were considerable, the antigens might well have been synthesized before the appearance of nucleoli in the erythrocyte nuclei. In that case, the observed association between the appearance of the nucleoli and the appearance of the surface antigens might simply be fortuitous. It was therefore obviously necessary to examine the behaviour of other proteins that might be determined by the erythrocyte nucleus, and especially soluble proteins that did not form part of a larger structural organization. A soluble enzyme was the obvious choice, and the enzyme inosinic acid pyrophosphorylase, which catalyzes the condensation of hypoxanthine with phosphoribosyl pyrophosphate, was chosen for study.[33] The enzyme is essential for the incorporation of hypoxanthine into nucleic acid and may thus be assayed either directly in a cell homogenate or indirectly in the intact cell by measuring the incorporation of labelled hypoxanthine. This enzyme was chosen because a line of mouse cells was available that lacked inosinic acid pyrophosphorylase activity (A_9 cells).[34]

When A_9 cells are exposed to tritiated hypoxanthine and then subjected to appropriate autoradiography, only a trivial amount of radioactivity is found to be incorporated into nucleic acid. When erythrocyte nuclei are introduced into irradiated A_9 cells, the heterokaryons also initially show very little incorporation of hypoxanthine. The enlargement and reactivation of the erythrocyte nuclei produce no change in this respect, until nucleoli make their appearance in the erythrocyte nuclei. When this occurs, the ability of the heterokaryons to incorporate hypoxanthine shows a sharp increase, and autoradiographs begin to show RNA labelling in many of the cells. This sequence of events is illustrated in Plates 15*a*, *b* and 16*a*. On further cultivation, the ability of the heterokaryons to incorporate hypoxanthine and the number of erythrocyte nuclei showing nucleoli continue to rise *pari passu* (Fig. 10). At all times, those heterokaryons in which the erythrocyte nuclei have not yet developed nucleoli show no significant increase in hypoxanthine incorporation (Fig. 11). Direct assay of the enzyme in cell homogenates confirms the findings obtained in intact cells by autoradiographic procedures. Very little inosinic acid pyrophosphorylase activity is initially detected in the heterokaryons, but when nucleoli begin to appear in the erythrocyte nuclei, the enzyme activity rises sharply and continues to rise as the development of nucleoli proceeds (Fig. 12). Electrophoretic examination of the enzyme formed in the heterokaryons confirms that it is chick, and not mouse, inosinic acid pyrophosphorylase.[35]

The fact that the soluble enzyme appears in the heterokaryons at the same time as the chick-specific surface antigen

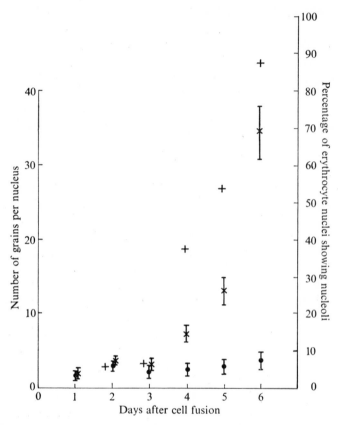

Fɪɢ. 10. The development of inosinic acid pyrophosphorylase activity in A$_9$-chick erythrocyte heterokaryons, as measured by their ability to incorporate tritiated hypoxanthine into nucleic acid. The incorporation of hypoxanthine in the heterokaryons is initially only marginally greater than that in A$_9$ cells alone; but when the erythrocyte nuclei develop nucleoli, this incorporation increases markedly. ●, A$_9$ cells; ×, heterokaryons; + erythrocyte nuclei showing nucleoli.

makes it very improbable that there can be any important lag, relative to the time scale on which these experiments are carried out, between the synthesis of the antigen and its appearance on the cell surface; and we are therefore faced with the conclusion that chick enzyme and chick antigen, which are neither structurally nor functionally related, both begin to be synthesized in the heterokaryon when nucleoli appear in the erythrocyte nuclei, and not before. The very fact that the anti-

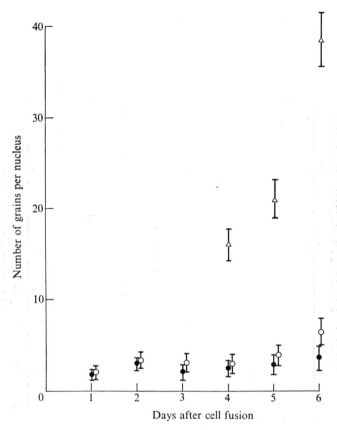

Fig. 11. A comparison between A_9-chick erythrocyte heterokaryons in which the erythrocyte nuclei have developed nucleoli and those in which they have not. The former show a marked increase in their ability to incorporate tritiated hypoxanthine; the latter are not much different from A_9 cells alone. ●, A_9 cells; △, erythrocyte nuclei showing nucleoli; ○, erythrocyte nuclei not showing nucleoli.

gen and the enzyme are so completely unrelated makes it unnecessary to entertain seriously the idea that the genes specifying these particular proteins begin to be transcribed only when a nucleolus appears in the erythrocyte nucleus. It is difficult to imagine why the transcription of just these genes should be delayed for some days and then begin simultaneously; nor are there any grounds for believing that these particular proteins are involved in nucleolar function. It seems much more

10—N.C.

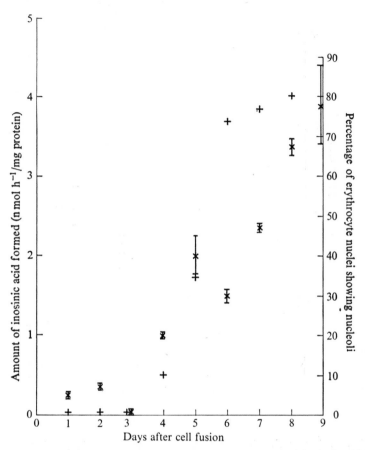

FIG. 12. The development of inosinic acid pyrophosphorylase activity in A_9-chick erythrocyte heterokaryons, as measured by direct assay of the cell homogenate. There is a marked increase in enzyme activity when the erythrocyte nuclei in the heterokaryon develop nucleoli. x, inosinic acid pyrophosphorylase activity; +, erythrocyte nuclei showing nucleoli.

reasonable to assume that the kinetics observed in the synthesis of these two unrelated proteins would also be observed with other proteins, and that the ability of the erythrocyte nucleus to determine the synthesis of *any* proteins would be conditional on the development of nucleolar activity. In any case, it was on this assumption that the investigation proceeded.

It was clearly of overriding importance to determine what

kind of RNA was made in the erythrocyte nuclei before and after they developed nucleoli. A technique was therefore devised to permit re-isolation of the nuclei from the heterokaryons and separation of the reactivated erythrocyte nuclei from the human or mouse nuclei.[29, 36] The heterokaryons were exposed to radioactive RNA precursors at various times after cell fusion, and the RNA synthesized in the two sorts of nuclei was examined by sucrose gradient centrifugation. It was found that while the human or mouse nuclei in the heterokaryon synthesized both 'rapidly labelled, polydisperse' RNA and the normal 28S and 16S RNA components, the erythrocyte nuclei, before the appearance of nucleoli, synthesized only 'polydisperse' RNA: normal 28S and 16S RNA began to be synthesized by these nuclei only when they developed nucleoli. Autoradiographic studies showed that the 'polydisperse' RNA made by the erythrocyte nuclei before development of nucleoli was synthesized, *grosso modo*, all over the nucleus and must therefore have contained the products of a very large number of genes. The RNA analyses thus posed a further paradox: 'polydisperse' RNA of high molecular weight, representing the activity of a very large number of genes, was synthesized by the erythrocyte nuclei for several days without determining the synthesis of species-specific proteins; but when the erythrocyte nuclei began to make RNA of ribosomal type (28S and 16S RNA), proteins specified by these nuclei began to be synthesized.

There appeared to be three possible explanations for these observations. The 'polydisperse' RNA made by the erythrocyte nuclei before development of nucleoli might not contain any RNA carrying instructions for protein synthesis. This explanation seemed unattractive, since it entailed the improbable consequence that the genes specifying proteins were not transcribed at all for several days and then, for some obscure reason, began to be transcribed simultaneously when the nucleolus made its appearance. Moreover, if the 'polydisperse' RNA did not at least include some RNA that carried instructions for protein synthesis, it was difficult to see where this RNA was to be found, since RNA having initially 'polydisperse' sedimentation was the only product that the great bulk of the genetic material appeared to synthesize. A second possibility was that the 'polydisperse' RNA did contain specifications for the synthesis of proteins, but that it was unable to programme the pre-existing ribosomes in the heterokaryons. Since the erythrocytes made no appreciable cytoplasmic contribution to these heterokaryons (mature erythrocytes, in any case, contain virtually no ribosomes), all the ribosomes initially present in the heterokaryons were human or mouse ribosomes; and it was conceivable that the RNA made on the chick chromosomes might not be able to programme human or mouse ribosomes. Hybrid cells have, however, been constructed in which a small amount of chick genetic material is introduced into a mouse cell; and in such hybrids the chick genes are able to determine the synthesis of chick enzyme even though the cells do not contain any chick 28S ribosomal RNA (which can be distinguished from mouse 28S ribosomal RNA by electrophoretic methods).[37, 38] It is therefore clear that RNA synthesized on chick genes can be translated by mouse cytoplasmic components. The third possibility was that the 'polydisperse' RNA did contain instructions for the synthesis of proteins, but that some nucleolar activity was essential for the transport of this RNA to the cytoplasm of the cell. On this view, the RNA made before the development of the nucleolus would fail to be transported to the cytoplasm of the cell and would be eliminated within the nucleus.

This last possibility was further investigated by means of experiments in which a microbeam of ultraviolet light was used to inactivate individual nuclei within the heterokaryon.[29, 39] If, before they developed nucleoli, the erythrocyte nuclei were unable to transfer the RNA that they synthesized to the cytoplasm of the cell, then 'anucleolate' erythrocyte nuclei in heterokaryons in which the human or mouse nuclei had been inactivated by the microbeam would not be expected to contribute to cytoplasmic RNA labelling when the cells were exposed to a radioactive RNA precursor; but these erythrocyte nuclei would be expected to contribute to cytoplasmic RNA labelling once they had developed nucleoli. Heterokaryons containing a single mouse nucleus and up to four reactivated erythrocyte nuclei were selected for study. The mouse nuclei were inactivated by the microbeam, and the level of cytoplasmic RNA labelling in the irradiated cells was measured after they had been exposed to a radioactive RNA precursor for periods up to 6 hours. In the same cultures normal mononucleate mouse cells in which the nucleus had also been inactivated by the microbeam served as controls, since, even in mononucleate cells, a low level of cytoplasmic RNA labelling persists after the nucleus has been irradiated. The measurements were made at various times after cell fusion: before any of the erythrocyte nuclei in the hetero-karyons had developed nucleoli; at a stage when some nucleoli were visible; and after many days when almost all erythrocyte nuclei showed well developed nucleoli. During the period in which the erythrocyte nuclei had not yet developed nucleoli, the level of cytoplasmic labelling in heterokaryons in which the mouse nucleus had been inactivated was indistinguishable from that found in normal mononucleate mouse cells in which the nucleus had been inactivated (Fig. 13). This was the case even in cells that contained several reactivated erythrocyte nuclei which collectively synthesized very large amounts of RNA as judged by the intensity of nuclear labelling in autoradiographs. It thus appeared that, prior to the development of nucleoli, the reactivated erythrocyte nuclei, although they synthesized large amounts of RNA continuously for some days, did not transfer detectable amounts of this RNA to the cytoplasm of the cell. A similar experiment, done at a stage when some of the erythro-cyte nuclei had developed nucleoli, showed that in some of the heterokaryons the level of cytoplasmic labelling after irradiation of the mouse nuclei was now significantly greater than in mono-nucleate cells in which the nuclei had been irradiated (Fig. 14); and when the great majority of the erythrocyte nuclei had developed nucleoli, cytoplasmic labelling in the heterokaryons after irradiation of the mouse nuclei was at an altogether higher level than that found in the irradiated mononucleate cells (Fig. 15). Plates 16b and 17a show the levels of cytoplasmic RNA labelling in an unirradiated heterokaryon and in a hetero-karyon in which the mouse nucleus was inactivated before the erythrocyte nucleus had developed a nucleolus. It will be seen that the erythrocyte nucleus continues to synthesize RNA but make no contribution to cytoplasmic RNA labelling. Plate 17b shows, for comparison, a heterokaryon in which the mouse nucleus was inactivated after the erythrocyte nucleus had developed a nucleolus. In this case, the erythrocyte nucleus does make a contribution to cytoplasmic RNA labelling. In the

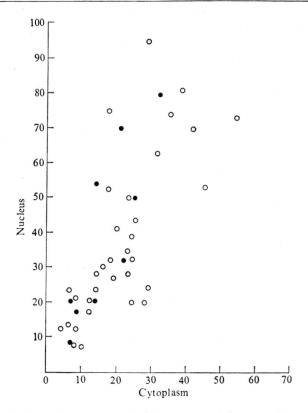

Fig. 13. Relationship between nuclear grain counts and cytoplasmic grain counts in heterokaryons and in single mouse cells. The heterokaryons contained one mouse nucleus and up to four chick erythrocyte nuclei that had been reactivated but had not yet developed nucleoli. The mouse nucleus was inactivated by ultraviolet light both in the heterokaryons and in the single mouse cells. The cells were exposed to a radioactive RNA precursor for 6 h. The ratio of nuclear to cytoplasmic RNA labelling in the heterokaryons in which the mouse nucleus had been inactivated was no different from that in the single mouse cells in which the nucleus had been inactivated. The reactivated erythrocyte nuclei, although they synthesize large amounts of RNA, do not make any detectable contribution to cytoplasmic RNA labelling at this stage. ◯, heterokaryons; ●, single mouse cells.

light of these experiments, the initial failure of the erythrocyte nuclei in the heterokaryons to determine the synthesis of specific proteins becomes understandable: it is not until these nuclei develop nucleoli that they acquire the ability to transmit genetic information to the cytoplasm of the cell.

The question, of course, at once arises whether this conclusion is restricted to erythrocyte nuclei reactivated under
these extraordinary conditions, or whether the nucleolus plays
a critical role in the transfer of genetic information in normal
mononucleate cells. It was thought possible that some more

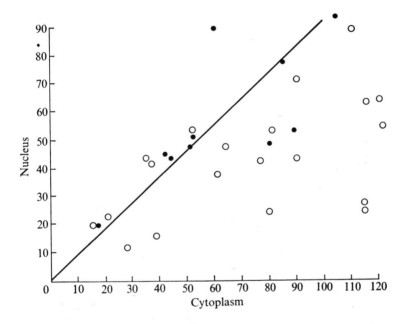

Fig. 14. A similar experiment to the one shown in Fig. 13, but done at an intermediate stage when some of the erythrocyte nuclei had begun to develop nucleoli.
It will be seen that the cytoplasmic labelling is now greater in some of the heterokaryons than in the single mouse cells. The reactivated erythrocyte nuclei are
beginning to contribute to cytoplasmic RNA labelling. ○, heterokaryons; ●,
single mouse cells.

direct evidence concerning the role of the nucleolus might be
obtained by using the microbeam to irradiate the nucleolus
alone. Normal mononucleate HeLa cells were chosen for this
study because many of these cells contained a single prominent
nucleolus which lent itself admirably to selective irradiation.
Nuclear and cytoplasmic RNA labelling were compared in four
groups of cells from the one culture: (1) unirradiated cells;
(2) cells with a single nucleolus that was selectively irradiated

with a dose of ultraviolet light sufficient to reduce its ability to synthesize RNA to less than 5 per cent of normal; (3) cells in which a non-nucleolar part of the nucleus (nucleoplasm) was given the same dose of irradiation with the same microbeam;

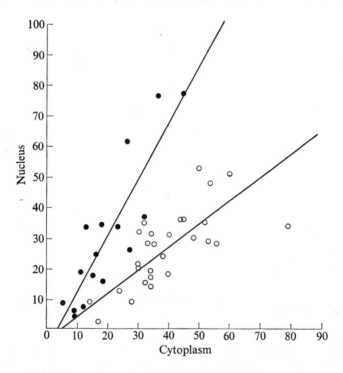

Fig. 15. A similar experiment to those shown in Figs. 13 and 14, but done at a stage when virtually all the erythrocyte nuclei had developed well-defined nucleoli. The cytoplasmic labelling in the heterokaryons is now decisively greater than in the single mouse cells. The erythrocyte nuclei are making a substantial contribution to cytoplasmic RNA labelling. ○, heterokaryons; ●, single mouse cells.

and (4) cells in which the whole nucleus was irradiated with a larger microbeam. The cells were again exposed to a radioactive RNA precursor for periods up to 6 hours after irradiation, and the pattern of RNA labelling analysed from autoradiographs. It was found that inactivation of the nucleolus alone reduced cytoplasmic RNA labelling by about 90 per cent, irrespective of the amount of RNA that continued to be synthesized in the rest of the nucleus (Fig. 16). This effect was not a non-specific consequence of the radiation, because comparable irradiation of the non-nucleolar part of the nucleus did not eliminate cytoplasmic RNA labelling. Irradiation of the whole nucleus, despite the much larger dose of ultraviolet light delivered to the

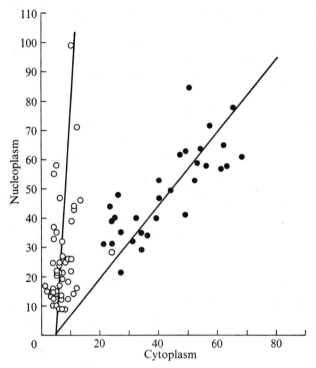

FIG. 16. Comparison of the number of grains over the cytoplasm with the number of grains over the non-nucleolar parts of the nucleus (nucleoplasm) in unirradiated HeLa cells (●) and in HeLa cells in which the nucleolus only was irradiated (○). The cells were exposed to a radioactive RNA precursor for 6 h. Irradiation of the nucleolus alone abolishes cytoplasmic RNA labelling, despite the fact that RNA synthesis continues in the rest of the nucleus.

cell, was hardly more effective in reducing cytoplasmic RNA labelling than irradiation of the nucleolus alone (Plate 18). The results thus showed that, in the absence of a functional nucleolus, the RNA synthesized in the rest of the nucleus was not transported in detectable amounts to the cytoplasm of the cell. These observations on the patterns of RNA labelling in mononucleate cells in which nucleolar activity was eliminated thus support the conclusions drawn from the experiments on erythrocyte nuclei reactivated in heterokaryons. The findings in both cases indicate that the nucleolus is involved in the transfer not only of the RNA made at the nucleolar site, but also of the RNA made elsewhere in the nucleus. Experimental error does not, of course, permit the statement that all the high molecular weight RNA made in the nucleus is dependent on nucleolar activity for its transport to the cytoplasm; but it does appear that the great bulk of the radioactivity incorporated into RNA in the extra-nucleolar regions of the nucleus fails to be transferred to the cytoplasm of the cell if the nucleolus is artificially inactivated or if it has not yet developed. It therefore seems very improbable that the RNA made in the nucleolus and the RNA made elsewhere in the nucleus can be transferred to the cytoplasm independently. The evidence indicates strongly that the transport of both these classes of RNA is co-ordinated by a single process that is located at or near the nucleolus.

These findings argue against any model for the transfer of information from nucleus to cytoplasm that postulates that the RNA carrying the information for protein synthesis diffuses from the nucleus into the cytoplasm and there attaches to pre-existing ribosomes; and they also argue against any model that postulates the passage of cytoplasmic ribosomes into the nucleus in order to release this RNA from the genes or serve as a vehicle for its transport to the cytoplasm. The chick erythrocyte nucleus in the heterokaryon does not begin to transfer detectable amounts of RNA to the cytoplasm of the cell and does not initiate the synthesis of chick-specific proteins until it develops its own nucleolus and begins to synthesize its own 28S RNA (and presumably its own ribosomes). The pre-existing ribosomes in the cytoplasm of the heterokaryon cannot accomplish the transfer of genetic information from the 'anucleolate' erythrocyte nucleus.

This fact has important consequences for our understanding of the mechanisms by which genetic information is expressed. The flow of genetic information from the nucleus to the cytoplasm of the cell appears to be coupled to the flow of ribosomes; and the flow of ribosomes appears in turn to be directly dependent upon the activity of the nucleolus. The nucleolus may thus be envisaged as the centre of some general regulatory mechanism that governs the flow, not only of structural RNA components, whatever these might be, but also of those components in the ribosomal complex that carry the specifications for protein synthesis. If, as the present evidence suggests, there is no independent flow of information to the cytoplasm of the cell, if the structural components of the ribosomal complex and those carrying the specifications for protein synthesis pass to the cytoplasm together, it follows that, under steady-state conditions, the RNA that carries the specifications for protein synthesis must have the same over-all stability in the cytoplasm as the other RNA components in the ribosomal complex. To seek to identify the RNA that carries the specifications for protein synthesis by its relative instability will, on this view, prove to be a search for a will o' the wisp. Moreover, if genetic information cannot pass to the cytoplasm without a concomitant flow of ribosomes, 're-programming' the cytoplasm of a cell must entail the replacement of one family of 'programmed' ribosomes by another. When cells are called upon to do something radically new, one would then expect to find not only an increase in the flow of ribosomal RNA from the nucleus, but also a breakdown of the ribosomal RNA already in the cytoplasm. And this is precisely what one does find.[40, 41]

The behaviour of erythrocyte nuclei reactivated in heterokaryons also sheds light on the puzzling phenomenon of intranuclear RNA turnover.[16, 42-47] If, in order to be transported to the cytoplasm of the cell, the RNA made on the chromosomes must first be 'engaged' by some mechanism that depends on nucleolar activity, the limiting step in the process of information transfer will not be the synthesis of the RNA that carries the genetic information, but the 'engagement' of this RNA by the nucleolar mechanism. And if the nucleolus is to play a regulatory role, which it clearly does, the 'engagement' mechanism must be sensitive to environmental influences, so that, as conditions change, a varying amount of the RNA made on the chromosomes fails to be 'engaged'. I should like to suggest that intranuclear RNA turnover is simply the intranuclear elimination of the RNA that fails to be 'engaged'. If this is so, one would expect intranuclear turnover of RNA to be more pronounced in nuclei that have a poorly developed nucleolar system or nuclei in which the nucleolar system has been impaired. The study of a wide range of experimental material confirms that this is indeed the case.[16, 29, 39, 48-53] But there is a difficulty. Although RNA having 'polydisperse' sedimentation properties appears to be the only primary product of the vast majority of genes, no RNA having the physical properties of this 'polydisperse' RNA can be detected in the cytoplasm of the cell. We must therefore assume, since information from at least some of these genes does reach the cytoplasm, that the 'polydisperse' RNA, during the process of 'engagement' and transfer to the cytoplasm, undergoes some secondary structural modifications that endow it with different sedimentation properties. How, then, are we to identify it in the cytoplasm of the cell? The experiments that indicate that the 'polydisperse' nuclear RNA has a mean chain length very similar to that of the 16S RNA,[54, 55] that it has the same over-all base composition,[56] and that it can be induced to sediment in the 16S position under appropriate conditions,[57] all suggest that the 'polydisperse' nuclear RNA may be represented in the cytoplasm by components that sediment in the 16S RNA region. But we do not at present have decisive evidence on this point; and we must await further analyses of the ribonucleic acids that sediment in the 16S region before we can accept this suggestion or dismiss it.

REFERENCES

1. HARRIS, H. and WATKINS, J. F. (1965). Hybrid cells from mouse and man: artificial heterokaryons of mammalian cells from different species. *Nature, Lond.* **205,** 640.
2. HARRIS, H. (1966). Hybrid cells from mouse and man: a study in genetic regulation. *Proc. R. Soc.* B **166,** 358.
3. HARRIS, H. (1965). Behaviour of differentiated nuclei in heterokaryons of animal cells from different species. *Nature, Lond.* **205,** 640.
4. HARRIS, H., WATKINS, J. F., FORD, C. E., and SCHOEFL, G. I. (1966). Artificial heterokaryons of animal cells from different species. *J. Cell Sci.* **1,** 1.
5. HARRIS, H., WATKINS, J. F., CAMPBELL, G. LE M., EVANS, E. P., and FORD, C. E. (1965). Mitosis in hybrid cells derived from mouse and man. *Nature, Lond.* **207,** 606.
6. HARRIS, H. (1970). *Cell fusion,* p. 19. Clarendon Press, Oxford.
7. OKADA, Y. (1958). The fusion of Ehrlich's tumor cells caused by H. V. J. virus *in vitro. Biken's J.* **1,** 103.
8. SCHNEEBERGER, E. E. and HARRIS, H. (1966). An ultrastructural study

of interspecific cell fusion induced by inactivated Sendai virus. *J. Cell Sci.* **1,** 401.

9. JOHNSON, R. T. and HARRIS, H. (1969). DNA synthesis and mitosis in fused cells. I. HeLa homokaryons. *J. Cell Sci.* **5,** 603.

10. JOHNSON, R. T. and HARRIS, H. (1969). DNA synthesis and mitosis in fused cells. II. HeLa-chick erythrocyte heterokaryons. *J. Cell Sci.* **5,** 625.

11. JOHNSON, R. T. and HARRIS, H. (1969). DNA synthesis and mitosis in fused cells. III. HeLa-Ehrlich heterokaryons. *J. Cell Sci.* **5,** 625.

12. WATKINS, J. F. and CHEN, L. (1969). Immunization of mice against Ehrlich ascites tumour using a hamster/Ehrlich ascites tumour hybrid cell line. *Nature, Lond.* **223,** 1018.

13. NABHOLZ, M., MIGGIANO, V., and BODMER, W. (1969). Genetic analysis using human–mouse somatic cell hybrids. *Nature, Lond.* **223,** 358.

14. MIGEON, B. R. and MILLER, C. S. (1968). Human–mouse somatic cell hybrids with single human chromosome (Group E): link with thymidine kinase activity. *Science, N.Y.* **162,** 1005.

15. SCHWARTZ, A. COOK, P. R., and HARRIS, H. (1970). Correction of a genetic defect in a mammalian cell. In press.

16. WATTS, J. W. and HARRIS, H. (1959). Turnover of nucleic acids in a non-multiplying animal cell. *Biochem. J.* **72,** 147.

17. GOWANS, J. L. and KNIGHT, E. J. (1964). The route of re-circulation of lymphocytes in the rat. *Proc. R. Soc.* B **159,** 257.

18. GOWANS, J. L., McGREGOR, D. D., COWEN, D. M., and FORD, C. E. (1962). Initiation of immune responses by small lymphocytes. *Nature, Lond.* **196,** 651.

19. CAMERON, I. L. and PRESCOTT, D. M. (1963). RNA and protein metabolism in the maturation of the nucleated chicken erythrocyte. *Expl Cell Res.* **30,** 609.

20. LANGHANS, T. (1868). Ueber Riesenzellen mit wandständigen Kernen in Tuberkeln und die fibröse Form des Tuberkels. *Virchows Arch. path. Anat. Physiol.* **42,** 382.

21. HARRIS, H. (1967). The reactivation of the red cell nucleus. *J. Cell Sci.* **2,** 23.

22. BOLUND, L., RINGERTZ, N. R., and HARRIS, H. (1969). Changes in the cytochemical properties of erythrocyte nuclei reactivated by cell fusion. *J. Cell Sci.* **4,** 71.

23. BOLUND, L., DARZYNKIEWICZ, Z., and RINGERTZ, N. R. (1969). Growth of hen erythrocyte nuclei undergoing reactivation in heterokaryons. *Expl Cell Res.* **56,** 406.

24. RINGERTZ, N. R. Personal communication.

25. RINGERTZ, N. R. and BOLUND, L. (1969). Activation of hen erythrocyte deoxyribonucleoprotein. *Expl Cell Res.* **55,** 205.

26. MITTWOCH, U., LELE, K. P., and WEBSTER, W. S. (1965). Relationship of Barr bodies, nuclear size and deoxyribonucleic acid value in cultured human cells. *Nature, Lond.* **205,** 477.

27. MITTWOCH, U. (1967). Barr bodies in relation to DNA values and nuclear size in cultured human cells. *Cytogenetics* **6,** 38.

28. MITTWOCH, U. (1968). Nuclear sizes in a human diploid/triploid cell culture. *Nature, Lond.* **219,** 1074.

29. HARRIS, H., SIDEBOTTOM, E., GRACE, D. M., and BRAMWELL, M. E. (1969). The expression of genetic information: a study with hybrid animal cells. *J. Cell Sci.* **4,** 499.

30. WATKINS, J. F. and GRACE, D. M. (1967). Studies on the surface antigens of interspecific mammalian cell heterokaryons. *J. Cell Sci.* **2,** 193.

31. ESPMARK, J. H. and FAGRAEUS, A. (1965). Identification of the species of origin of cells by mixed haemadsorption: a mixed antiglobulin reaction applied to monolayer cell cultures. *J. Immun.* **94,** 530.

32. COOMBS, R. R. A., MARKS, J., and BEDFORD, D. (1956). Specific mixed agglutination: mixed erythrocyte-platelet antiglobulin reaction for the detection of platelet antibodies. *Br. J. Haemat.* **2,** 84.

33. HARRIS, H. and COOK, P. R. (1969). Synthesis of an enzyme determined by an erythrocyte nucleus in a hybrid cell. *J. Cell Sci.* **5,** 121.

34. LITTLEFIELD, J. W. (1964). Three degrees of guanylic acid-inosinic acid pyrophosphorylase deficiency in mouse fibroblasts. *Nature, Lond.* **203,** 1142.

35. COOK, P. R. (1970). Species specificity of an enzyme determined by an erythrocyte nucleus in an interspecific hybrid cell. *J. Cell Sci.* In press.

36. FISHER, H. W. and HARRIS, H. (1962). The isolation of nuclei from animal cells in culture. *Proc. R. Soc.* B **156,** 521.

37. SCHWARZ, A., COOK, P. R., BRAMWELL, M. E., and HARRIS, H. In preparation.

38. BRAMWELL, M. E. In preparation.

39. SIDEBOTTOM, E. and HARRIS, H. (1969). The role of the nucleolus in the transfer of RNA from nucleus to cytoplasm. *J. Cell Sci.* **5,** 351.

40. TATA, J. R. (1970). Hormonal control of metamorphosis. *Ciba symposium on control processes in multicellular organisms,* p. 131. Churchill, London.

41. COCUCCI, S. M. and SUSSMAN, M. (1970). RNA in cytoplasmic and nuclear fractions of cellular slime mold amoebae. *J. molec. Biol.* **45,** 399.

42. HARRIS, H. (1959). Turnover of nuclear and cytoplasmic ribonucleic acid in two types of animal cell, with some further observations on the nucleolus. *Biochem. J.* **73,** 362.

43. HARRIS, H. and WATTS, J. W. (1962). The relationship between nuclear and cytoplasmic ribonucleic acid. *Proc. R. Soc.* B **156,** 109.

44. HARRIS, H., FISHER, H. W., RODGERS, A., SPENCER, T., and WATTS, J. W. (1963). An examination of the ribonucleic acids in the HeLa cell with special reference to current theory about the transfer of information from nucleus to cytoplasm. *Proc. R. Soc.* B **157,** 177.

45. HARRIS, H. (1963). The breakdown of RNA in the cell nucleus. *Proc. R. Soc.* B **158,** 79.

46. HARRIS, H. (1963). Nuclear ribonucleic acid. *Prog. nucl. Acid Res.* **2,** 20. Academic Press, New York.

47. HARRIS, H. (1964). Breakdown of nuclear ribonucleic acid in the presence of actinomycin D. *Nature, Lond.* **202,** 1301.

48. EDSTRÖM, J. E. (1965). Chromosomal RNA and other nuclear RNA

fractions. *Role of the chromosomes in development* (Ed. M. Locke), p. 137. Academic Press, New York.

49. Bruns, G. P., Fischer, S., and Lowy, B. A. (1965). A study of the synthesis and interrelationships of ribonucleic acids in duck erythrocytes. *Biochim. biophys. Acta* **95,** 280.

50. Attardi, G., Parnas, H., Hwang, M., and Attardi, B. (1966). Giant-size rapidly labelled nuclear RNA and cytoplasmic messenger RNA in immature duck erythrocytes. *J. molec. Biol.* **20,** 145.

51. Karasaki, S. (1968). The ultrastructure and RNA metabolism of nucleoli in early sea urchin embryos. *Expl Cell Res.* **52,** 13.

52. Kijima, S. and Wilt, F. H. (1969). Rate of nuclear ribonucleic acid turnover in sea urchin embryos. *J. molec. Biol.* **40,** 235.

53. Perry, R. P. (1963). Selective effects of actinomycin D on the intracellular distribution of RNA synthesis in tissue culture cells. *Expl Cell Res.* **29,** 400.

54. Tamaoki, T. and Lane, B. G. (1967). The chain termini and alkali-stable dinucleotide sequences in rapidly labeled ribonucleates from L cells. *Biochemistry, N.Y.* **6,** 3583.

55. Riley, W. T. (1969). Polynucleotide chain lengths of rapidly labelled and ribosomal RNA of mammalian cells and *E. coli*. *Nature, Lond.* **222,** 446.

56. Bramwell, M. E. and Harris, H. (1967). The origin of the polydispersity in sedimentation patterns of rapidly labelled nuclear ribonucleic acid. *Biochem. J.* **103,** 816.

57. Bramwell, M. E. (1970). Intranuclear accumulation of RNA resembling the smaller ribosomal RNA component. *J. Cell Sci.* **6,** 53.

6. Differentiation

1. Definitions

WHEN an experimentalist begins to be worried about the way scientific terms are used and attempts restrictive definitions of them, his colleagues are apt to shake their heads and conclude that his days as an experimentalist are numbered. But it seems to me that I cannot fail to increase the confusion that surrounds the use of certain common terms in embryology if I refrain from discussing the ideas that underlie the use of these terms; and I must, in any case, make clear the restrictions that I intend to impose on these terms in this chapter. Differentiation is commonly defined as the process by which, during the development of the individual from the fertilized ovum, specialized cells, tissues, and organs are formed. The word was first, and is still, most commonly used in connection with the growth of multicellular organisms, and thus implies the production from a single cell, the ovum, of progeny that exhibits increasing heterogeneity as the individual develops. But a biologically equivalent process also takes place in some unicellular organisms. In these, a part of the cell may undergo morphological and functional specialization to form a structure that exists also in multicellular organisms, but is composed, in the latter, of large numbers of cells. I propose to use the term differentiation to describe this process of specialization, whether it occurs in unicellular or multicellular organisms. When we come to use the terms 'differentiated', 'undifferentiated', and 'dedifferentiated', it is not so easy to delineate a precise empirical content. If one defines the ovum as *the* undifferentiated cell, then cells become differentiated as they acquire characters that permit them to be distinguished from the ovum and from each other; but since the two daughters resulting from the first division of the ovum can easily be distinguished from the ovum itself, if only by the difference in size, it is the second feature, that is, the development of recognizable heterogeneity within the progeny of the ovum, that is commonly used to define the onset of cellular differentiation. This is, of course, simply a convention. The ovum is itself the product of a complex process of differentiation within the ovary, and it would be possible to construct a terminology with some other cell as the reference point. Assuming the conventional frame of reference, however, I shall define undifferentiated cells as those descendants of the ovum that have not yet developed recognizable heterogeneity, and differentiated cells as those that have. 'Dedifferentiation' is more difficult and involves a much vaguer frame of reference. Of course, a differentiated cell does not ever revert to a fertilized ovum, or even to one of its early descendants, so that, *sensu stricto*, the word is a misnomer. But, under certain conditions, differentiated cells that show one or more specialized characteristics lose these characteristics and may acquire others. In some cases this transformation superficially resembles a partial reversal of the process of differentiation in that a cell that has acquired a specialized characteristic at some stage of differentiation comes to resemble, at least superficially, an earlier ancestor that lacked this particular characteristic. It is not at all clear that this sort of transformation does indeed represent a reversion to an ancestral cell type: we may merely be observing the loss of some easily recognizable properties and their replacement by others that are less striking. I shall therefore use the word 'dedifferentiation' sparingly, and simply to describe the loss of some easily recognizable feature or features in a differentiated cell, without necessarily implying thereby that any reversal of the process of differentiation has taken place.

2. *Changes in DNA*

The simple observation that some of the changes produced by differentiation were very stable and could persist through many cell generations suggested to early investigators of this problem that differentiation might be the result of progressive alterations in the genetic material of the cell. This view gained some support from the fact that differentiation in some cells was accompanied by obvious morphological changes in the nucleus and the chromosomes. A more contemporary and more precise statement of this position would be that the events that determine the process of differentiation are changes in the nucleotide sequences of the DNA of the cell. In the case of one special form of differentiation, the formation of antibodies by cells of the lymphoid series, the view is commonly held that some form of somatic variation in the nucleotide sequences of the DNA determines the specificity of the antibody; but the general theory that differentiation as a whole is determined by changes in the DNA now has few adherents. It is, of course, common knowledge that many plants can be propagated vegetatively by cuttings from different parts of the plant. In some cases, small fragments from almost any part of the plant will regenerate a whole new plant. It is thus at once clear that completely differentiated tissues in these plants contain at least some cells which under appropriate conditions can give rise to progeny showing all the forms of differentiation that characterize the complete plant. In more recent years this has been demonstrated also for small groups of cells[2-4] and, in certain cases, for single cells,[5-7] cultivated *in vitro*. These small groups of cells or single cells produce a callus from which the whole plant can sometimes be grown. In some of the experiments in which whole plants were grown from single cells, these were originally differentiated cells in that they showed morphological features characteristic of their tissue of origin.[5, 6] In animals the evidence is less dramatic, but it leads to the same conclusion. Nuclei isolated from cells of a renal tumour of the adult frog (the Lucké carcinoma) can be transplanted into enucleated frog eggs, where they will support development to the stage of the feeding tadpole;[8-10] and nuclei from cells of the intestinal epithelium of the tadpole have been shown to support the development of mature and even fertile toads.[11, 12] We may therefore conclude that if differentiation depends upon changes in the nucleotide sequences of the DNA of the cell, these changes are not irreversible. But only four kinds of changes involving the nucleotide sequences of DNA are known: deletion, addition, and substitution of nucleotides, and their transformation *in situ*. We must therefore envisage an elaborate and directed progression of such changes during the course of differentiation and their accurate reversal when differentiated cells resume activities in which they were engaged earlier in their development. Nothing that we know about changes involving DNA in biological material provides any ground for believing that a process of this sort exists. In the current state of our knowledge, the ability of the nuclei of some differentiated cells to support the development of a whole plant or a whole animal must be regarded as strong evidence that differentiation is not achieved by progressive modification of the nucleotide sequences of DNA.

3. Differentiation and regulation

We are then left, in principle, with three other possibilities: differentiation might be produced by selective transcription of different parts of the DNA at different times, so that some templates are made available at one time and others at another; or it might be produced by selective translation of different templates at different times; or it might be produced by both of these mechanisms. Now this is ground that I have already covered in Chapter 4, when I discussed the regulation of protein synthesis; but, although differentiation clearly involves such regulation, it poses two additional problems that I have not yet mentioned. Most studies that have been made in recent years on the regulation of protein synthesis have involved the use of systems in which the maintenance of a change in protein synthesis is dependent upon the continued presence of the stimulus that induced the change. For example, a particular small molecule may induce the synthesis of a particular protein, but the synthesis of this protein stops when the small molecule is removed; or another small molecule may repress the synthesis of the protein, but synthesis is resumed when this small molecule is removed. Although differentiation obviously includes changes of this sort, it also involves changes that persist after the stimulus or stimuli that initiated them have been removed. In some cases, the initial stimulus sets in train a complex chain of reactions in which the synthesis of a specific protein is a terminal event occurring many hours or days after the original stimulus has ceased to exist. This phenomenon embryologists call *determination*. The second characteristic feature of differentiation is that phenotypic changes produced in the cell by a particular stimulus may be maintained through many cell generations after the stimulus has been removed; and, in some cases, these changes may be maintained indefinitely.

I should like to illustrate these two special features of differentiation with some examples. If a dorsal pancreatic rudiment, containing both epithelium and mesenchyme, is dissected from an 11-day mouse embryo and then cultivated *in vitro* on a porous membrane, the cells of the rudiment will differentiate into typical pancreatic tissue showing both the structural and functional characteristics of normal pancreas. By the second day after explantation ultrastructural changes indicative of differentiation can be observed in the epithelial cells; by the third day the amylase activity of the explants is about 100 times that present initially; and between the fourth and fifth day typical zymogen granules appear.[13] If the mesenchyme is removed from the fragment prior to explantation, then the remaining epithelium fails to differentiate in this way. But if the mesenchyme is maintained in contact with, or in close proximity to, the epithelium for the first 48 h after explantation, all subsequent stages of differentiation proceed normally even when the mesenchyme is removed.[13,14] It is clear that the mesenchyme in this case provides a stimulus to differentiation, but, once the chain of events has been initiated, it goes to completion even if the stimulus is no longer present. Suspensions of presumptive muscle cells (myoblasts) can be made from chick embryo muscle tissue, and these cells can then be grown as a monolayer on a glass surface. They have initially a morphology resembling that of fibroblasts and do not show the characteristic striations or enzymatic reactions of muscle; nor do they undergo contractions. The cells grow on the glass without undergoing any morphological change until the monolayer becomes confluent, at which stage fusion takes place between adjacent cells to give rise to multinucleate cells. These then develop striations, acquire enzymatic activities characteristic of muscle and undergo vigorous contraction.[15,16] In this case, an initial stimulus to muscle formation has occurred in the embryo, but overt differentiation is held in abeyance through several cell generations until appropriate cultural conditions for complete differentiation are achieved.

On the other hand, it is a common observation that differentiated cells showing certain specialized morphological or biochemical features may undergo 'dedifferentiation', that is, the loss of these specialized features, when they are explanted and grown in artificial culture. The prevalence of observations of this sort at one time gave rise to the idea that the differentiated state could not be maintained in prolonged culture outside the body. Recent investigations have made it clear that in at least some cases the failure to propagate differentiated cells *in vitro* was due to the fact that in artificial culture these cells were at a selective disadvantage relative to other cells in the population, and were consequently overgrown.[17] When steps were taken to overcome this selective disadvantage it became possible to grow differentiated cells, showing specific biochemical and morphological features, for many months, if not indefinitely, *in vitro*. The cell lines that appear capable of indefinite multiplication without loss of the differentiated state have all so far been derived from differentiated tumours;[17-20] but muscle cells, cells that form pigment and cells that form cartilage have been grown for many months from diploid cells isolated directly from the embryo.[21-23] It is thus clear that, in principle, a highly differentiated state can be maintained not only through many generations of cells in the body, where it could be argued that the cells remain subject to continuous inductive stimuli, but also *in vitro* where, at least under certain conditions of culture, such stimuli cannot be present.

4. Genetic activity and differentiation

Having thus delineated these two cardinal features of differentiation, I should like now to examine what fragmentary data we have on these problems, to see whether they throw any light on the underlying mechanisms that might be involved. To my mind, by far the most illuminating experiments on differentiation have been carried out in unicellular organisms; and, for the most decisive observations, we must return once again to the giant unicellular alga, *Acetabularia* (see Chapter 1). You will recall that this cell grows for many weeks by elongation of its stalk, and then, under appropriate conditions, undergoes differentiation to form a fruiting-body or cap by means of which its spores are disseminated. The formation of the cap is a classical example of differentiation involving dramatic morphological and biochemical changes; it is in every way comparable to the formation of similar fruiting bodies in related multicellular organisms. Now I have already pointed out that in *Acetabularia* growth of the stalk and complete differentiation of the species-specific cap can take place long after the cell nucleus has been removed. We can therefore conclude at once that in this organism the overt stages of differentiation do not result from differential transcription of the genetic material. The stalk is not formed at a particular time because at that time stalk-forming genes are being transcribed; and the cap is not formed at another time because at that time cap-forming genes are being transcribed. The genes involved in forming both the stalk and the cap are obviously transcribed long before the overt events themselves take place. Experiments that I have already described on the induction of premature caps indicate that all the genes necessary for cap formation must be transcribed in some species of *Acetabularia* at least 70 days before the cap is normally formed;[24] and experiments on the accumulation and storage of information in the cell cytoplasm indicate that, for a large part of the period of growth of the cell, the templates for both stalk formation and cap formation are delivered to the cytoplasm continuously.[25] Moreover, formation of the cap can be held in abeyance indefinitely if the cells are maintained at low levels of illumination. This permits continued growth of the stalk, which may thus become very much longer than normal. Such grossly elongated stalks can be induced to form caps by an increase in the level of illumination, even after they have been enucleated.[26] These observations make it quite clear that in *Acetabularia* the overt act of differentiation is elaborated by the cytoplasm of the cell on pre-existing templates, and that this elaboration does not require the presence of the relevant genes.

This state of affairs, as I have pointed out before, is not limited to *Acetabularia*. Most unicellular organisms which survive enucleation for any length of time appear to be capable of at least some measure of differentiation. Where differentiation involves the co-operation of a number of cells, enucleation of the differentiating tissue is obviously not possible, so that we have no observations in multicellular organisms as decisive as those that have been made on *Acetabularia* or *Stentor*.[27] But the experiments that demonstrate the failure of high concentrations of actinomycin D to inhibit decisive events in the differentiation of colonial myxamoebae,[28] of pancreatic cells in the mouse embryo,[29, 30] and of haemoglobin-forming cells in the chick embryo,[31] argue strongly in favour of the view that in multi-cellular organisms also at least the overt stages of differentiation do not require concomitant genetic activity.

We are therefore thrown back once again on the problem of how cytoplasmic regulatory mechanisms might operate, and, more especially, how early changes in the cytoplasm impose an ordered sequence of subsequent events. We have glimpses of this kind of organization in the phenomenon of 'sequential induction' (induction *en chaîne*) of enzymes in bacteria.[32] Here, members of a group of related enzymes are formed sequentially when the first enzyme of the series has been induced; and it is generally thought that the end product of each enzyme, or some related compound, is the inducer for each subsequent enzyme.[33] While such phenomena may well be involved in differentiation, the analogy cannot, however, be pressed too closely. The persistence of an induced sequence of enzymes in bacteria remains dependent on the presence of the initial inducer, whereas differentiation is characterized by progressive independence of the initial stimulus. Moreover, differentiation characteristically produces structural changes in the cell and progressively involves many very different groups of enzymes. Structural changes often appear to be at the heart of the process, and the electron microscope may reveal reorganization of the pattern of ribosomal particles in the cytoplasm, or the development of ordered membrane systems, some time before the overt features of the differentiated state make their appearance.[34, 35] The only processes in bacteria that are at all analogous to differentiation in higher cells are sporulation and germination. I have already discussed in Chapter 2 the close similarity between sporulation and germination in bacteria and the corresponding processes in eukaryotic organisms; and I have reviewed the evidence which indicates that sporulation and germination, once initiated, become progressively independent of continued genetic activity. We may therefore hope that the continued study of these processes in bacteria will contribute to our knowledge of differentiation in higher cells, even if the study of genetic regulation in vegetative bacterial cells at present appears to be only marginally relevant.

5. Co-ordination in multicellular organisms

In one respect differentiation in multicellular organisms poses a special problem. While it is altogether probable that the fundamental biochemical basis of any particular type of differentiation will be the same whether it occurs in a unicellular or multicellular organism, in the latter case we have also to explain how co-operation between a large number of individual cells is actually achieved. There are two ways in which this can be done: either all the cells are individually exposed to the same stimuli at the same time in the same way; or the cells interact with each other to ensure a corporate response to any given stimulus. The second alternative is, of course, intrinsically more probable; and there is now convincing experimental evidence that interaction between cells is not only a means of achieving a corporate response, but is, in some cases, an essential requirement for the process of differentiation itself. For example, I have described how a pancreatic rudiment from the mouse embryo, explanted into artificial culture under appropriate conditions, will differentiate into functional pancreatic tissue.[13,14] If this rudiment is cut into smaller pieces, which are then cultivated separately, differentiation of the epithelium into pancreatic cells does not take place. But if these fragments are grown close together, so that they fuse again into a single mass, then differentiation will proceed.[13,36] Similar effects are also seen with other epithelia.[37] It is clear that differentiation in these cases requires large scale co-operative activity between cells, and that single cells, or small groups of cells, cannot achieve the conditions necessary to permit the differentiation to occur.

Some experiments by Loewenstein and his colleagues[38-41] have greatly illuminated our understanding of how this co-operative activity might be achieved. These authors, using microelectrodes to measure the voltage drop across individual cell membranes, have established that there is virtually free passage of electrolytes from cell to cell in epithelia from a wide range of different sources: salivary glands and renal tubules of diptera, sensory epithelium in the ampullae of Lorenzini (large sense organs) of elasmobranchs, urinary bladder of the toad, larval skin of urodeles, and both normal and regenerating liver parenchyma of the rat. This intercellular flow of electrolytes appears to take place through specialized regions of contact between adjacent cell membranes. These regions are known as 'tight-junctions' and, under the electron microscope, they exhibit different forms of structural modification in different tissues. It has, moreover, been demonstrated that these junctions permit the passage not only of small ions, but also of much larger dye molecules and perhaps even of macromolecules of the dimensions of proteins and nucleic acids.[42] These epithelial tissues may therefore be regarded as functionally unified systems; and it is possible that the essentially regional character of each successive step in the differentiation of multicellular organisms may be determined by the range over which any particular system of intercellular communication extends. Some recent measurements on intercellular communication in developing embryos lend some support to this suggestion.[43-45]

6. Stimuli for differentiation

A frame of reference in which the ovum is regarded as *the* undifferentiated cell has the disadvantage that it tends to encourage an underestimate of the structural and functional complexity of the ovum itself. If one is accustomed to thinking of the ovum as undifferentiated, one tends to assume that the progressive imposition of diversity in the progeny of the ovum must require an elaborate sequence of highly specific signals and a correspondingly elaborate system of genetic switches. Indeed, some optimistic molecular biologists have even suggested that to explain differentiation one has simply to determine which genes are switched on and when. At least as far as the early steps in differentiation are concerned, this idea appears to be very improbable: the evidence does not at present encourage the belief that genetic switches are important determinants in the observed sequence of events. Although the data so far available are rather preliminary, they lead one to suppose that in a wide range of biological material all the organization necessary for the early stages of embryonic development is present in the cytoplasm of the ovum before it is fertilized. The only decisive test that we have at present for detecting when new genetic instructions are given in the developing embryo is to determine when markers of paternal origin make their appearance. Many enzymes show species or strain specificities that are revealed by differences in electrophoretic mobility, heat stability, or other physical properties. When sperm and ovum are derived from species that show such differences in a particular enzyme, analysis of the nature of the enzyme synthesized in the zygote will reveal when new genetic information for that enzyme passes to the cytoplasm and is translated; for when this occurs, paternal as well as maternal enzyme will be synthesized. While the number of such studies is so far very limited, they concur in showing that paternal enzymes become detectable only at relatively advanced stages of embryonic development. In the sea-urchin egg, the enzymes responsible for digestion of the coat during hatching of the embryo are still apparently entirely of maternal type.[46] In amphibia paternal enzymes do not appear until development of the embryo has proceeded to the stages of muscle movement and heart beat;[47] and in interspecific fish and bird hybrids, paternal enzymes also appear only at a late stage of embryonic development.[48] No doubt more sensitive methods will reveal the presence of paternal markers somewhat earlier, but it seems very likely that the development of the embryo to a relatively advanced stage is achieved essentially on a basis of maternal information, that is, information that was delivered to the cytoplasm of the egg before formation of the heterozygotic nucleus. During these stages of development it is therefore very likely that differentiation is achieved not by switches that initiate the transcription of structural genes in the nucleus, but by switches that initiate the expression of a programme that is already present in the egg cytoplasm.

What kind of signals are likely to be responsible for the initiation of one cytoplasmic programme rather than another? It will be obvious that the degree of specificity that these signals need have will be a function of the number of alternative programmes that a cell is at any one time capable of executing. If, for example, the ovum itself or its early progeny were capable of expressing a very wide range of different phenotypes, then the signals governing the development of the early embryo would have to show a corresponding range of specificity;

but if the alternative modes of development confronting the
ovum or its early progeny are at any one time very limited,
then simple signals of very low specificity would be enough to
determine the execution of one cytoplasmic programme rather
than another. It appears probable that the alternatives facing
the cells of the early embryo are in fact very limited (progression to ectoderm, entoderm, or mesoderm); and it is only
after these primary differentiations have been achieved that the
cells are faced with other sets of alternative possibilities. If this
is so, one would expect that the signals governing the early steps
in differentiation would have a very low specificity; and, even
in the later stages of differentiation, highly specific signals
might not become necessary provided the number of alternative
choices facing any particular cell at any one time is not large.
That simple signals can achieve very complex patterns of differentiation is well illustrated by the behaviour of explants
taken from the coelenterate *Hydra viridis*.[49] Explants containing
only two cell types can, in appropriate defined media, be induced to regenerate a whole animal. Analysis of this regeneration *in vitro* reveals that the direction of differentiation of the
two cell types is determined by the ionic composition of the
medium itself: different ionic environments determine different
modes of differentiation. Electrolyte movements also appear to
be involved in the differentiation of early amphibian embryos.
Major changes in intracellular sodium ion concentration
occur in the developing embryo when the coelom is formed
in the blastocyst; and these changes are accompanied by alterations in cell metabolism.[50] It is therefore possible that
electrolyte movements might be a common form of signal
for early events in embryonic development. As differentiation
proceeds, a system of signals that flow from one cell to another
becomes operative. We see examples of this form of communication in even the most primitive forms of multicellular
differentiation. For example, the life cycle of certain cellular
slime moulds includes a stage in which the unicellular amoeboid cells aggregate to form a multicellular fruiting body.
This aggregation is initiated when some of the amoeboid
cells emit a chemotactic substance (recently identified as
cyclic adenosine monophosphate) which is recognized by the
surrounding cells.[51, 52] In *Hydra*, nerve cells in and around the

peduncle emit a diffusible substance, apparently a peptide, which influences the multiplication and differentiation of cells elsewhere in the body of the organism.[53,54] I have already mentioned the effect of substances released by the mesenchyme in determining the differentiation of pancreatic epithelium in the mouse embryo.[13,14] A voluminous literature records similar effects in other embryonic and regenerating tissues.

As far as can be judged from the data available, all these signals appear to operate, not by inducing the transcription of a new genetic programme, but by initiating the execution of a programme that has already been delivered. In this respect, embryonic development does not appear to differ in principle from the differentiation of the cap in *Acetabularia* or the formation of the fruiting body in *Dictyostelium*. The transcription of the genes relevant to a particular event in the process of differentiation generally occurs long before the arrival of the signals that initiate that event. As I have already mentioned, most of the genes involved in determining the early stages of embryonic development appear to be transcribed before fertilization of the egg. Other genes may be transcribed continuously, as appears to be the case for the genes governing the formation of both stalk and cap in *Acetabularia*;[24,25] others again may cease to be transcribed as selective condensation in different regions of the nuclear chromatin takes place. Our knowledge of transcriptional sequences in embryonic development is nugatory.

7. Heritable differentiation

Perhaps the most difficult feature of differentiation to explain is the fact that some differentiated characteristics are heritable and, apparently, heritable indefinitely. It must, however, be stressed that heritability is by no means a general characteristic of differentiated traits. Some forms of differentiation are incompatible with cell multiplication, and are thus never inherited. For example, the onset of haemoglobin synthesis in a cell sets in train a sequence of events that results in complete suppression of protein and nucleic acid synthesis, and, in some orders of vertebrate, even in elimination of the cell nucleus. In adult animals there are several families of highly differentiated cells that appear never to undergo mitosis and never give rise to tumours. On the other hand, most tissues that are capable of regeneration give rise to tissues of the same kind: liver cells multiply to produce more liver cells. None the less, it is a commonplace observation of tumour pathology that tumours which grow rapidly, and especially the secondary deposits which they form, frequently lose the distinctive features of the tissue from which they originate. It is not at present clear to what extent this process represents 'dedifferentiation' in the sense previously defined, and to what extent it is simply the result of progressive selection for those cells in a mixed population in which the features of the differentiated state are less pronounced. In any case, it is clear that some differentiated states are eliminated quite rapidly during cell multiplication and others persist for long periods. In many cases persistence of the differentiated state involves the persistence of tissue organization, that is, of the co-operative activity of large numbers of cells in the manner that I have discussed. It can always be argued that, within the body, persistence of differentiation through several cell generations, even when the cells are dislodged from their normal site, is due to the continued action of stimuli that induce or maintain the differentiated state in each cell generation. This appears, on the face of it, to be rather farfetched in at least some cases, but it does formally reduce the discussion of heritable differentiated states to those cases in which these states are maintained through prolonged periods of cell multiplication *in vitro*. There are rather few such cases; but they constitute the crux of the problem.

I have already presented the reasons for rejecting the idea that the differentiated state results from changes in the nucleotide sequences of DNA, so that some mechanism of inheritance must be sought other than that provided by the self-replication of DNA. A simple solution, and one that has frequently been advanced in the past, is that some of the RNA templates in the cytoplasm might be capable of self-replication. This idea at present finds little favour, but even if it proved none the less to be correct, we should still be left with the problem of explaining why some templates undergo self-replication and others do not, and why particular templates undergo self-replication under particular sets of circumstances. In other words, we should still have to explain why a given cytoplasmic state persists, or fails to persist, under different conditions. And we should still have to explain this, even if we adopted the model of differentiation based on differential transcription of the DNA. If we suppose that a particular differentiated state is achieved by the selective transcription of certain genes, and not others, the persistence of this state through many cell generations implies that the selective transcription is maintained; and this in turn entails that the factors that select one range of genes for transcription, rather than another, are also maintained. On any model, then, we are forced to consider how a set of conditions, initially produced in a cell by external stimuli, can become self-generating. It may be that there is no single general answer to this problem: that different sets of conditions may become self-generating by different mechanisms, and that there may be many such mechanisms.

I should like to consider three cases of this phenomenon in unicellular organisms. In *E. coli*, as I have previously discussed in some detail, the synthesis of the enzyme β-galactosidase can be induced by substrates of the enzyme and certain other related compounds. The enzyme, once induced, continues to be synthesized at a maximal rate so long as the inducer compounds are present, but ceases to be synthesized as soon as these compounds are removed, or are exhausted from the medium. Induction of the enzyme normally also involves induction of a 'permease' system in the cell membrane, which serves to maintain an adequate concentration of the inducer within the cell. If the enzyme and the 'permease' system are once induced in a cell by the inducer, the concentration of this inducer in the medium can then be reduced to levels well below those normally required to initiate induction, but the cells remain induced and the enzyme continues to be synthesized at the maximal rate for many generations.[55] The induction of the 'permease' system provides an intracellular concentration of inducer sufficient to determine continued maximal synthesis of the enzyme even when the external concentration of the inducer is inadequate. In this case we have an example of a stable cytoplasmic change, involving synthesis of a specific enzyme, imposed by the establishment of a new equilibrium in an existing metabolic pathway. The second case concerns the formation of the cell wall in *B. subtilis*. If these organisms are treated with the enzyme lysozyme, their cell walls are dissolved and 'protoplasts', bounded simply by the cell membrane, are formed. In suitable media these protoplasts can be cultivated indefinitely, or at least for very long periods, as 'L-forms' that lack the normal cell wall. When, however, the L-forms are transferred to a solid medium containing hard agar or gelatin, they will revert, virtually quantitatively, to the usual bacillary forms producing a normal cell wall.[56-58] The loss of the ability to form the cell wall appears to be associated with the disappearance from the cytoplasm of the cell of specific membranous structures, known as 'mesosomes', which appear to be essential for the formation of the wall.[59-61] The conversion of the bacillary form of the organism to the L-form and the subsequent reversion of the latter do not entail what are normally called genetic changes. The third case involves observations on the pattern of synthesis of surface antigens in *Paramecium*. The surface of this organism normally contains a number of different antigens, which are present in a variety of alternative states. In any one strain of *Paramecium*, one group of antigens may be present under certain conditions, and another group under other conditions. If organisms showing one type of antigenic pattern are incubated for a short time at a higher temperature, or are briefly exposed to specific antisera, the pattern of antigens on their surface may change; and the progeny of these organisms, even when grown under the same conditions as the original culture, will then continue to show the new antigenic pattern.[62] In other words, exposure of these cells to a higher temperature or to antiserum induces a cytoplasmic change that results in the replacement of one group of surface antigens by another, and this change is heritable. Thus we have examples of heritable cytoplasmic changes involving in one case the acquisition of the ability to synthesize a particular enzyme, in another the loss of the ability to synthesize a particular structure, and in the third the substitution of one group of antigens by another. I think it likely that the detailed mechanism underlying the change will prove to be different in each of these cases; and I think it reasonable to suppose that other cases of this type of inheritance may well be determined by still different mechanisms.

These self-generating states in unicellular organisms are, of course, very reminiscent of the cases that I have already described in which a differentiated state in an animal cell may be maintained through a prolonged, or even indefinite, period of cultivation *in vitro*.[16-23] We do not have any solid information about the biochemical mechanisms by which these differentiated states are established and maintained in animal cells; but experiments in which cells differentiated in a particular way are fused with other cells are beginning to provide an approach to the analysis of this problem.[63] Not only the differentiated state itself may be maintained through successive generations of cells cultivated *in vitro*, but also the capacity to undergo a specific form of differentiation in response to an appropriate stimulus (heritability of *determination*). For example, cells derived from a mouse testicular teratocarcinoma may be cultivated for long periods *in vitro* without showing any of the morphological features of the teratocarcinoma; but these cells produce tumours with characteristic teratomatous patterns of differentiation when they are injected into the animal.[19] Heritability of determination has been studied most extensively in the cells of the 'imaginal discs' of larvae of *Drosphila*.[64] These larval structures eventually differentiate to form the tissues of the adult fly, but their differentiation can be held in abeyance by continuous culture in the abdominal cavity of the adult fly. The discs can be subcultivated from fly to fly indefinitely without undergoing differentiation; but when the cells from such an explant are returned to the larva they undergo the pattern of differentiation characteristic of the particular imaginal disc from which they were originally derived. In this case the whole programme for a specific form of differentiation is carried indefinitely in each of the cells of the explanted disc, and the cells simply require the appropriate signal provided by the larval environment to execute the programme which they carry. Occasionally these cells do execute a different programme (a phenomenon known as *transdetermination*), but a wide range of experiments indicates that the number of different programmes that the cells of any one imaginal disc can carry out is very limited. These observations thus support the view that at any one time a differentiating cell is faced with few alternative possibilities and that the signals determining the execution of one pattern of differentiation rather than another might, even for very complicated programmes of development, be relatively simple.

8. Nuclear changes in differentiation

Finally, I should like to consider the nuclear changes that take place during differentiation. These changes may be morphological, but they may also involve partial or total inhibition of the transcription of DNA. I have argued that these restrictions on the transcription of DNA in higher cells are essentially coarse control mechanisms involving the condensation of large areas of the genetic material and associated, in at least some cases, with changes in nuclear volume. I now wish to say that, in my view, these restrictions on RNA synthesis in the cell nucleus are not the cause of differentiation, but its consequence. I cannot envisage how these gross processes, which simultaneously suppress the activity of thousands of genes or of whole chromosomes or of whole sets of chromosomes, can be responsible for determining the highly ordered, subtle, and precise cytoplasmic changes that take place during differentiation. But it is not difficult to imagine how accumulation of haemoglobin within a cell might produce progressive condensation of the nucleus and thus progressive inhibition of RNA synthesis. Of course, the suppression of RNA synthesis in one part of the nucleus and its continuation in another will have phenotypic consequences. Interruption of the flow of templates from one part of the nucleus will obviously alter the balance of templates within the cytoplasm of the cell; and this could determine the loss of certain cytoplasmic functions. It is therefore altogether reasonable to talk about a continuous interaction between nucleus and cytoplasm; but this type of interaction is a far cry from the model that envisages a vast array of highly specific genetic switches, each immediately determining the onset of some precise step in the process of differentiation. Nothing that I know about the behaviour of cells leads me to suppose that differentiation is produced in this way. If, in this spring of 1970, we still have a very imperfect understanding of differentiation, this, in my view, is because we are still looking too hard at the cell nucleus and not hard enough at the cytoplasm.

REFERENCES

1. *Antibodies: Cold Spring Harb. Symp. quant. Biol.* (1967). **32,** *passim.*
2. STEWARD, F. C., MAPES, M. O., and SMITH, J. (1958). Growth and organized development of cultured cells. I. Growth and division of freely suspended cells. *Am. J. Bot.* **45,** 693.
3. STEWARD, F. C., MAPES, M. O., and MEARS, K. (1958). Growth and organized development of cultured cells. II. Organization in cultures grown from freely suspended cells. *Am. J. Bot.* **45,** 705.
4. STEWARD, F. C. (1958). Growth and organized development of cultured cells. III. Interpretations of the growth from free cell to carrot plant. *Am. J. Bot.* **45,** 709.
5. VASIL, V. and HILDEBRANDT, H. C. (1965). Differentiation of tobacco plants from single isolated cells in microcultures. *Science, N.Y.* **150,** 889.
6. JOSHI, P. C. and BALL, E. (1968). Growth of isolated palisade cells of *Arachis hypogaea in vitro. Devl Biol.* **17,** 308.
7. REINERT, J. (1968). Morphogenese in Gewebe- und Zellkulturen. *Naturwissenschaften* **55,** 170.
8. KING, T. J. and McKINNELL, R. G. (1960). An attempt to determine the developmental potentialities of a cancer cell nucleus by means of transplantation. *Cell physiology neoplasia,* p. 591. University of Texas Press.
9. McKINNELL, R. G. (1962). Development of *Rana pipiens* eggs transplated with Lucké tumor cells. *Am. Zool.* **2,** 430.
10. McKINNELL, R. G., DEGGINS, B. A., and LABAT, D. D. (1969). Transplantation of pluripotential nuclei from triploid frog tumors. *Science, N.Y.* **165,** 394.
11. GURDON, J. B. (1962). The developmental capacity of nuclei taken from intestinal epithelium cells of feeding tadpoles. *J. Embryol. exp. Morph.* **10,** 622.
12. GURDON, J. B. and UEHLINGER, V. (1966). 'Fertile' intestine nuclei. *Nature, Lond.* **210,** 1240.
13. GROBSTEIN, C. (1964). Cytodifferentiation and its controls. *Science, N.Y.* **143,** 643.
14. FELL, P. E. and GROBSTEIN, C. (1968). The influence of extra-epithelial factors on the growth of embryonic mouse pancreatic epithelium. *Expl Cell Res.* **53,** 301.
15. KONIGSBERG, I. R. (1960). The differentiation of cross-striated myofibrils in short-term cell structure. *Expl Cell Res.* **21,** 414.
16. KONIGSBERG, I. R. (1961). Some aspects of myogenesis *in vitro. Circulation* **24,** 447.
17. YASUMURA, Y., TASHJIAN, A. H., and SATO, G. H. (1966). Establishment of four functional, clonal strains of animal cells in culture. *Science, N.Y.* **154,** 1186.
18. MOORE, G. E. (1964). *In vitro* cultures of a pigmented hamster melanoma cell line. *Expl Cell Res.* **36,** 422.
19. STEVENS, L. C. (1960). Embryonic potency of embryoid bodies derived from a transplantable testicular teratoma of the mouse. *Devl Biol.* **2,** 285.

20. RICHARDSON, U. I., TASHJIAN, A. H., and LEVINE, L. (1969). Establishment of a clonal strain of hepatoma cells which secrete albumin. *J. Cell Biol.* **40,** 236.
21. CAHN, R. D. and CAHN, M. B. (1966). Heritability of cellular differentiation: clonal growth and expression of differentiation in retinal pigment cells *in vitro. Proc. natn. Acad. Sci. U.S.A.* **55,** 106.
22. COON, H. G. (1966). Clonal stability and phenotypic expression of chick cartilage cells *in vitro. Proc. natn. Acad. Sci. U.S.A.* **55,** 66.
23. YAFFE, D. (1968). Retention of differentiation potentialities during prolonged cultivation of myogenic cells. *Proc. natn. Acad. Sci. U.S.A.* **61,** 477.
24. WERZ, G. (1965). Determination and realization of morphogenesis in *Acetabularia. Brookhaven Symp. Biol.* No. 18, p. 185.
25. HÄMMERLING, J. and ZETSCHE, K. (1966). Zeitliche Steuerung der Formbildung von *Acetabularia. Umschau* **15,** 489.
26. HÄMMERLING, J. (1963). Nucleo-cytoplasmic interactions in *Acetabularia* and other cells. *A. Rev. Pl. Physiol.* **14,** 65.
27. TARTAR, V. (1961). *The biology of* Stentor, p. 297. Pergamon Press, Oxford.
28. SUSSMAN, M. and SUSSMAN, R. R. (1965). The regulatory program for UDP galactose polysaccharide transferase activity during slime mold cytodifferentiation: requirement for specific synthesis of ribonucleic acid. *Biochim. biophys. Acta* **108,** 463.
29. WESSELLS, N. K. and WILT, F. H. (1965). Action of actinomycin D on exocrine pancreas cell differentiation. *J. molec. Biol.* **13,** 767.
30. RUTTER, W. J., WESSELLS, N. K., and GROBSTEIN, C. (1964). Control of specific synthesis in the developing pancreas. *J. natn. Cancer Inst. Monogr.* No. **13,** p. 51.
31. WILT, F. H. (1965). Regulation of the initiation of chick embryo hemoglobin synthesis. *J. molec. Biol.* **12,** 331.
32. STANIER, R. Y. (1951). Enzymic adaptation in bacteria. *A. Rev. Microbiol.* **5,** 35.
33. MANDELSTAM, J. and JACOBY, G. A. (1964). Induction and multisensitive end-product repression in the enzymic pathway degrading mandelate in *Pseudomonas fluorescens. Biochem. J.* **94,** 569.
34. KALLMAN, F. and GROBSTEIN, C. (1964). Fine structure of differentiating mouse pancreatic exocrine cells in transfilter culture. *J. Cell Biol.* **28,** 399.
35. WESSELLS, N. K. and EVANS, J. (1968). Ultrastructural studies of early morphogenesis and cytodifferentiation in the embryonic mammalian pancreas. *Devl Biol.* **17,** 413.
36. WESSELS, N. K. and COHEN, J. H. (1967). Early pancreas organogenesis: morphogenesis, tissue interactions and mass effects. *Devl Biol.* **15,** 237.
37. DEUCHAR, E. M. (1970). Effect of cell number on the type and stability of differentiation in amphibian ectoderm. *Expl Cell Res.* **59,** 341.
38. LOEWENSTEIN, W. R. and KANNO, Y. (1964). Studies on an epithelial (gland) cell junction. I. Modifications of surface membrane permeability. *J. Cell Biol.* **22,** 565.

39. LOEWENSTEIN, W. R., SOCOLAR, S. J., HIGASHINO, S., KANNO, Y., and DAVIDSON, N. (1965). Intercellular communication: renal, urinary bladder, sensory, and salivary gland cells. *Science, N.Y.* **149**, 295.
40. LOEWENSTEIN, W. R. and KANNO, Y. (1967). Intercellular communication and tissue growth. I. Cancerous growth. *J. Cell Biol.* **33**, 225.
41. LOEWENSTEIN, W. R. and PENN, R. D. (1967). Intercellular communication and tissue growth. II. Tissue regeneration. *J. Cell Biol.* **33**, 235.
42. KANNO, Y. and LOEWENSTEIN, W. R. (1966). Cell-to-cell passage of large molecules. *Nature, Lond.* **212**, 629.
43. SHERIDAN, J. D. (1968). Electrophysiological evidence for low-resistance intercellular junctions in the early chick embryo. *J. Cell Biol.* **37**, 650.
44. ITO, S. and LOEWENSTEIN, W. R. (1969). Ionic communication between early embryonic cells. *Devl Biol.* **19**, 228.
45. LOEWENSTEIN, W. R. (1968). Emergence of order in tissues and organs. *Devl Biol. Suppl.* **2**, p. 151.
46. BARRETT, D. and ANGELO, G. M. (1969). Maternal characteristics of hatching enzymes in hybrid sea urchin embryos. *Exp. Cell Res.* **57**, 159.
47. WRIGHT, D. A. and SUBTELNY, S. (1969). Expression of genes controlling enzymes in diploid and androgenetic haploid hybrid frog embryos. *J. Cell Biol.* **43**, 160a.
48. OHNO, S. (1969). The preferential activation of maternally derived alleles in development of interspecific hybrids. *Heterospecific genome interaction, Wistar Institute Symposium Monograph* No. 9, p. 137. Wistar Institute Press, Philadelphia.
49. BURNETT, A. L. (1968). The acquisition, maintenance and lability of the differentiated state in *Hydra*. *The stability of the differentiated state* (Ed. H. URSPRUNG), p. 109. Springer-Verlag, Berlin.
50. KOSTELLOW, A. B. and MORRILL, G. A. (1968). Intracellular sodium ion concentration changes in the early amphibian embryo and the influence of nuclear metabolism. *Expl Cell Res.* **50**, 639.
51. BONNER, J. T. (1947). Evidence for the formation of cell aggregates by chemotaxis in the development of the slime mould *Dictyostelium discoideum*. *J. exp Zool.* **106**, 1.
52. KONIJN, R. M., BARKLEY, D. S., CHANG, Y. Y., and BONNER, J. T. (1968). Cyclic AMP: a naturally occurring acrasin in the cellular slime moulds. *Am. Nat.* **102**, 225.
53. BURNETT, A. L., DIEHL, N., and DIEHL, F. (1964). The nervous system of *Hydra*. II. Control of growth and regeneration by neurosecretory cells. *J. exp. Zool.* **157**, 227.
54. LESH, G. E. and BURNETT, A. L. (1966). An analysis of the chemical control of polarized form in *Hydra*. *J. exp. Zool.* **163**, 55.
55. NOVICK, A. and WEINER, M. (1957). Enzyme induction as an all-or-none phenomenon. *Proc. natn. Acad. Sci. U.S.A.* **43**, 553.
56. LANDMAN, O. E. and HALLE, S. (1963). Enzymically and physically induced inheritance changes in *Bacillus subtilis*. *J. molec. Biol.* **7**, 721.
57. MILLER, I. L., ZSIGRAY, R. M., and LANDMAN, O. E. (1967). The formation of protoplasts and quasi spheroplasts in normal and chloramphenicol-pre-treated *Bacillus subtilis*. *J. gen. Microbiol.* **49**, 513.

58. TICHY, P. and LANDMAN, O. E. (1969). Transformation in quasi spheroplasts of *Bacillus subtilis. J. Bact.* **97,** 42.

59. RYTER, A. and LANDMAN, O. E. (1964). Electron microscope study of the relationship between mesosome loss and the stable L state (or protoplast state) in *Bacillus subtilis. J. Bact.* **88,** 457.

60. LANDMAN, O. E., RYTER, A., and FRÉHEL, C. (1968). Gelatin-induced reversion of protoplasts of *Bacillus subtilis* to the bacillary form: electron-microscopic and physical study. *J. Bact.* **96,** 2154.

61. MILLER, I. L., WIEBE, W., and LANDMAN, O. E. (1968). Gelatin-induced reversion of protoplasts of *Bacillus subtilis* to the bacillary form: photomicrographic study. *J. Bact.* **96,** 2171.

62. BEALE, G. H. (1957). The antigen system in *Paramecium aurelia. Inter. Rev. Cytol.* **6,** 1.

63. HARRIS, H. (1970). *Cell fusion,* pp. 48–56. Clarendon Press, Oxford.

64. GEHRING, W. (1968). The stability of the determined state in cultures of imaginal disks in *Drosophila. The stability of the differentiated state* (Ed. H. URSPRUNG), p. 136. Springer-Verlag, Berlin.

Author Index

Subject Index

frog,
  enucleate eggs of, 11, 144
  oocytes of, 11
  pituitary hormones and, 11
fruiting body,
  in *Dictyostelium*, 41
  in myxomycetes, 41

galactoside permease gene (*y*), 29
galactoside transacetylase gene (*a*), 29
gamma radiation, 122
gelatin, 157
generation time,
  of animal cells, 35
  of *E. coli*, 35
genes,
  closely linked, 41
  clustering of, 29, 40
  of *E. coli*, 29, 30, 31
   clustering of, 29
   mutations of, 31
   operon in, 30
   order of, 29, 31
  selective transcription of, 156
genetic activity, 147–50
genetic code, 70
genetic information, 1, 9
genetic instructions, 2
'genetic operator' model, 21–42
  applicability to higher cells, 87
genetic regulation, specificity of, 86
genetic switches, 151
germination, 41, 42, 149
  in microcysts of *Myxococcus xanthus*, 42
  in wheat embryos, 42
globin, 12, 83
'glucose' effect, 26
glutamine synthetase, of embryonic chick neural retina, 14
glycerol, 26
Gram negative bacteria, 22, 82
  clusters of related genes in, 22
growth response, to androgens in chick comb, 14
guanylic acid, 48

haem, 12, 83
haemoglobin, 159
  -forming cells of chick embryo, 149
  synthesis, 154
   in chick embyro explants, 15
   in mammalian reticulocyte, 12
  messenger RNA for, 68

haemolysis, 115
haemolytic action of 'Sendai' virus, 116
heavy nitrogen, 48
HeLa cells, 107, 108, 111, 112
hen-specific antigens, 121
  disappearance of, 121
  displacement by human or mouse antigens, 121
  reappearance of, 122
heritable differentiation, 154–9
heterogeneity, 143
heterogeneous RNA, 69
heterogeneous sedimentation behaviour, 58
heterokaryons, 108, 114, 119, 125, 130
  A₉–chick erythrocyte, 126, 127, 128
  cytoplasmic labelling of, 132, 134
  DNA synthesis in, 108, 109
  HeLa-hen erythrocyte, 112
  HeLa-rabbit, macrophage, 112
  HeLa-rat lymphocyte, 112
  macrophage-erythrocyte, 114
  macrophage-lymphocyte, 115
  protein synthesis in, 108
  RNA synthesis in, 108
high molecular weight RNA, 136
  transport to cytoplasm, 136
histidine biosynthesis, 82
histidine locus, 81
histidyl-transfer RNA, 82
homogenization, 66
hybrid cells, 106–8, 110–15
  differentiated, 107, 110–15
  interspecific, 106–8, 116
  man–mouse, 106, 110
   genes of, 108
  mouse–chick, 110
  mouse–hamster, 110
  mononucleate, 109–10
  multinucleate, 107, 108
  undifferentiated, 107
  with human and murine nuclei, 108
hybrid cytoplasm, 116
  signals of, 116
   false, 116
   transmission of, 116
Hydra viridis, 153
  nerve cells, 153
hypoxanthine, 125
  incorporation of, 125